The History of
The Tendring Show

ONE HUNDRED NOT OUT

First published in Great Britain as a softback original in 2015
Copyright © Guy and Elizabeth Smith
The moral right of this author has been asserted.
All rights reserved.

Published by UK Book Publishing
UK Book Publishing is a trading name of Consilience Media
www.ukbookpublishing.com

ISBN: 978-1-910223-45-1

Langham

Dedham

Maningtree

E N

Lamford

Ardle

R. Way to Norwich

T E

Little Bromley

Elmsted

Great Bromley

Great sted

Little Bentley

E D

oyland

East Downland

Wivenhoe

Frating

H U

Great Bentley

Alresford

Kings

Therington

R E E N

Brightlinsea

Langenhoe

The Priory

D R E D

East Morsea

RIVER STOUR

HARWICH

Thorn

Wisbuss

adfield

Dovor Cort

Ramsey

NX D Wicks R I N G

Little Oakley

Great Oakley

Horsey Island

Bramont cum Moe

Waltons Tower

triny Homstalle

N D . R E D

Kirby

Thorp

Walton

Weeley

Frinton

Great Holland

Little Clackton

Great Clackton Little Holland

lyth

XV

Contents

Introduction

The Show held on 11th July 2015 at Lawford House Park is the 100th Tendring Show. It marks a striking achievement for what is widely regarded as one of the best one day shows in the country. But it has not all been plain sailing since the first show in Thorpe Hall in 1899. Two World Wars, Foot and Mouth Disease, rival shows and a lack of funds have all caused shows to be cancelled. Of course, the fickle English summer weather has also done its bit to frustrate the best laid plans - not to mention marquee fires, swine fever, stolen takings and riderless horses! But somehow the farmers of the Tendring Hundred have persevered to make sure their show survived while others did not. Tracing its origins back to a cattle show and ploughing match in a meadow behind Thorpe Church in the 1830s, 'One Hundred - Not Out' tells the story of the Tendring Show spanning three centuries of immense change. From the early years when the Show changed grounds every year moving right across the district while attracting both Royalty and leading politicians, to the post-war revival when the Show established itself as a major event attracting crowds of 25,000 - the Tendring Show has always stayed true to its roots while not getting stuck in its ways. While the farmers of the Tendring Hundred have seen their farming transform out of all recognition, they have remained dedicated to the tradition of their show, recognising it as a vital opportunity to show off the best of local agriculture as well as a treasured occasion to celebrate a vibrant rural life. As the Show looks forward to another century of success it is time to celebrate a century of achievement. 'One Hundred Not Out' has a nice ring to it.

Chapter One

ORIGINS

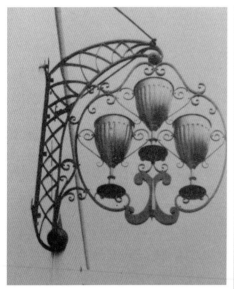

The Three Cups Hotel.

Our story starts in the summer of 1898 in the Three Cups Hotel which sat at the top of Colchester's main thoroughfare - the High Street. The Three Cups was a large rambling coaching Inn of Georgian origin that claimed to be Colchester's premier inn. It had been bought by the neighbouring Corn Exchange in the 1880s who had slapped an over ornate facade onto its face as was the fashion in Victorian times. Located close to the Livestock Market at the bottom of North Hill and next door to the Corn Exchange, the Three Cups would have attracted farmers when they had a day 'in town' selling beasts or corn. In amongst these visiting Essex yeoman there would undoubtedly have been farmers from across the Tendring Hundred for whom Colchester was the nearest commercial centre.

Just as today, farmers in these late Victorian times would have spent most of their days working in isolation from each other and would have had much to discuss when they met up over a pint of beer or something stronger. No doubt the weather was the usual topic of conversation but seeing as July and August 1898 had provided near perfect hot, dry harvesting weather the farmers might have needed something else to moan about.

John Eagle...

One farmer who frequented the Corn Exchange as well as the Live Market and the Three Cups was John Eagle from Walton Hall. Walton Hall sat on the nose of Walton-on-the-Naze, the most easterly point of the Tendring peninsula. Eagle was a keen breeder of Suffolk Sheep and, as was the habit of those who sold pedigree stock, he showed his prize winning animals at local shows. The nearest show for him, as it was for the rest of his Tendring Hundred farming brethren, was at Hadleigh. Hadleigh was a fair hike of twenty miles for Eagle and his sheep. Eagle had come to the firm view that a fine farming area like the Tendring Hundred should have its own show. With its easy working soils, its flat terrain and its benign climate the area was not short of good farmers and good farming. Eagle had the fortune of sharing his ideas and ambitions with his friend, Herbert Wenden who farmed at Morehams Hall in Frating. We know from his civic work elsewhere that Wenden was both a man who knew how to organise as well as being a man who got things done.

...and his prize winning Suffolk Sheep

Between them they decided to call a meeting at the Corn Exchange on Saturday 22nd October to discuss the issue of the Tendring Hundred's lack of a show. Saturday was market day when farmers were in town. At that

What remains of the Colchester Corn Exchange today - the frontage of a Bank.

meeting it was agreed that they should form a 'Farmers Club and Agricultural Association for the Tendring Hundred'. Eagle was to be the first Chair and Wenden the Secretary. We can only assume there was a decent turn out because a committee of cleven was appointed with each member representing three of the thirty three parishes of the Tendring Hundred. A yearly membership of 10 shillings was agreed and within a few months there were an encouraging two hundred members. Most importantly, plans were then put in place to organise a show the following year. This was to prove to be the very first Tendring Show. Today, history suggests that Eagle and Wenden laid good foundations because by the year 2015 there would be ninety nine more. Unfortunately the Three Cups Hotel lacked such staying power and was demolished in the 1960s to be replaced by some faceless piece of architectural inanity. The Corn Exchange fared a little better with some of the original frontage still recognisable today but it now houses a bank. However, before we move our story on to that first show in 1899 let us go back in time so we can better understand how in 1898 Tendring Farmers were so readily enthused to hold a show.

First it would be appropriate to explain how the area became known as the Tendring Hundred. Both a small village and an administrative area surrounding it bear the name. The favoured theory amongst those who study these things is that the name 'Tendring' comes from the old Saxon word for tinder because the place was known as a good place to gather dry wood. It seems a good theory in as much that we know that a thousand years ago the area had extensive deciduous woodland and that, just as today, it was known for its dry weather. While we are on the subject of weather, it might be worth noting that the Royal Commission on the state of agriculture noted in 1805 that the climate of Essex was 'generally mild; however its northerly and easterly winds in the County's north east quarter are pernicious to the point that crops are prone to blight and the human species are prone to colds and hoarseness'.

The derivation of the title 'Hundred' is more certain than where the name 'Tendring' comes from. A 'Hundred', of which Essex has several,

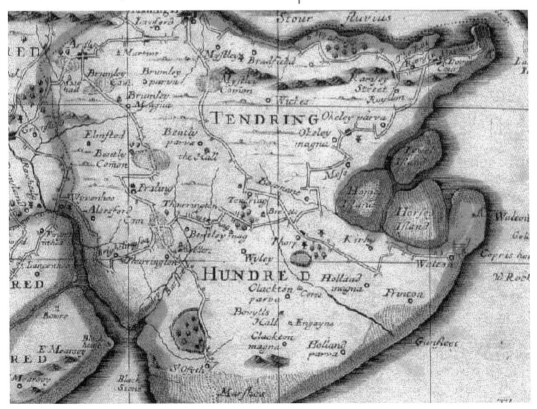

is an administrative area of Government established during the reign of Alfred the Great in the 880s. The title derives from the fact that a hundred families occupied the area. Under Alfred's wise Kingship, this system of dividing his domain into Hundreds meant his subjects answered to the community within the Hundred, thus giving a primary structure for local government and a legal system. Today, the old Anglo-Saxon division of Hundreds is largely forgotten but in Tendring the geography of the place ensures it lives on.

How the boundaries of the Tendring Hundred were established is also straight forward because 80% of them are coast. The Tendring peninsula is a bubble of land to the east of the ancient town of Colchester with the Stour and Colne estuary to the north and south and the German Ocean, as it was called until 1914, lapping against its eastern shore. Thus the

St. Osyth Priory in 1907. The Priory had been a focal point in the Tendring Hundred since medieval times. It provided a venue for the Tendring Show in 1914 and 1923.

Tendring Hundred is a rough circle of 80,000 acres surrounded by the sea. Being a peninsula and an outpost, the district has always had an air of self containment. Until the Victorian era with the advent of transport for the masses, it was thinly populated with just 25,000 people. But at the same time it was not a backwater in that through the ancient port of Harwich at its northern end it had one of Britain's key links to the Continent. The Three Cups Hotel that we mentioned at the beginning of this story boasts Kings, Queens and Ambassadors as its most famous guests. They were usually on their way to London having arrived from the continent at Harwich. Harwich can also boast a very famous M.P. - Samuel Pepys, the nations most famous diarist. Nearby Manningtree can also claim a five star literary association in that William Shakespeare in his play Henry IV made mention of the famous 'Manningtree Ox'. At the other end of the peninsula lay another focal point of national importance - St. Osyth Priory. With its expansive lands, St. Osyth Priory attracted powerful religious institutions in medieval times and then with the dissolution of the monasteries in the 1500s it attracted powerful families such as the Rochfords and the Darcys who frequented Royal Courts. As a final literary connection we might mention the name 'Mr. Darcy'. When Jane Austen was thinking of names for her hero and heroine in her novel Pride and Prejudice she was obviously aware that in the seventeenth century Bryan Darcy had been involved in the hanging of a local woman as a witch - her name being Elizabeth Bennett.

A Contemporary Etching of The Swing Riots.

But let us return to the farmers of the Tendring Hundred and their desire to put on a show. Whether they knew it or not, when in 1898 Eagle and Wenden discussed the need for a farmers club and an agricultural show in Tendring, they were not without precedent because there had been something very similar some sixty years previously.

The 1830s were tumultuous times for Tendring farmers. Prices were very depressed leading to economic anxiety. Furthermore there was considerable unrest among agricultural labourers who were losing their jobs on the back of the economic downturn and due to mechanisation. This was the time of the notorious Swing Riots when working men took their vengeance on the new thrashing machines that were taking their jobs by smashing them with hammers. Although most of the rioting took place in Kent and Sussex, the Tendring Hundred had its own episodes. There were incidences of rick burning in Little Clacton. Then in February 1830 a rabble of several hundred labourers rampaged through Walton and Kirby Le Soken smashing farm equipment and eventually surrounding a group of farmers in the Red Lion pub. Understandably the farmers initially agreed to the mob's demands for jobs and better pay. Once the incendiary mood of the rabble had dampened down, the farmers called in the local militia who rounded up the ring leaders who were subsequently tried and sent to far away Tasmania. This episode was a reminder to local farmers of the need to unite and organise.

Another cause for alarm in farming circles at this time were the growing calls for the Repeal of the Corn Laws. The Corn Laws kept the price of wheat artificially high by placing a duty on imported wheat. As Britain shifted from being an agrarian nation to an industrial one in the first half of the nineteenth century, the industrialists and factory owners were taking political power from the land owning aristocracy. Based around Manchester in the north these industrialists favoured free trade and saw no reason why flour and bread should be made more expensive through import duties. The farmers and landowners saw this as an attack on them and protested that free trade would ruin home agriculture by sucking in imports thus threatening the nations food security. Protectionist societies were set up across the country in support of keeping the Corn Laws. The idea was

Thorpe High Street in Victorian times with The Maids Head towards the end of the street on the left. The Maids Head was a meeting place for both the Tendring Hundred Agricultural Association in the 1840s and the Tendring Hundred Farmers Club in the 1900s.

A ploughing match in the 1850s.

that they would petition Parliament on behalf of local landowners and farmers. One such society was 'The Tendring Hundred Agricultural Association' formed in 1832 at the Maids Head in Thorpe-Le-Soken. While meetings of the THAA were regularly held to discuss the affairs of the day and to send Parliament petitions it was clear that this new agricultural association was more than just about politics. It can also be seen as part of a movement in early nineteenth century Britain that saw a burgeoning of interest in science and experiment when it came to improving farming. New ideas about managing soils and plants were emerging. Breed societies that encouraged improved pedigree breeding of farm livestock were established.

To harness this new interest in improving agriculture new associations of farmers were established. Indeed many of our nations agriculture shows can trace their origins from around this time. The Suffolk Agricultural Association was formed in 1831 while The Hadleigh Farmers Agricultural Association was established in 1839. Most grandly the Royal Agricultural Society of England held the nations first national show in 1840. The newly formed Tendring Hundred Agricultural Association was, in its modest local way, very much part of this movement. Every June from 1832 to 1849 it held a show in and around the village of Thorpe. As part of this a cattle show was held in a meadow next to the church while ploughing matches and sheep sheering competitions were staged just up the road at

Thorpe Hall. Reports tell us that crowds of up to two thousand would attend. In the afternoon a large tent was erected on the meadow where around two hundred farmers drawn from across the Tendring Hundred would sit down to a hearty luncheon. After the meal 'the cloth was removed' and toasts were drunk. In amongst all the toasts, heartfelt speeches about the state of agriculture were made interspersed with songs such as the recently penned popular ditty 'Life's a Bumper'. Finally Cups and Prizes were given out for the best beasts in the show not forgetting the best ploughmen and sheep shearer. Interestingly money was also presented to farm labourers who had shown 'fulsome

The Maids Head.

loyalty to their masters'. No doubt the social unrest in Kirby and Little Clacton in 1830 were very much on farmers minds when this was done. There were also prizes for men who had raised children without 'poor relief'. The resourceful and fertile farm labourer, Thomas Bareham, deserves mentioning as he managed to raise a family of thirteen without resorting to this early form of social welfare.

The Tendring Hundred Agricultural Association seemed a lively group. Apart from the annual cattle show they also met during the winter at the Maids Head to discuss the affairs of the day. The village of Thorpe Le Soken was a sensible place to meet as it was central in the Tendring Hundred. It was, in a way, the local capital. District Courts could be found operating in Thorpe along with other aspects of early local Government.

For reasons we don't know the Association lost popularity in the late 1840s. The Essex Standard Newspaper of the 8th June 1849 reports that the Show that year was a 'shadow of its former self' with 'the smallest attendance ever witnessed'. There was no cattle show as funds didn't allow it. There was a ploughing match and a luncheon but only a hundred or so attended. There were no more shows held after this. The last mention we can find of the THAA is in 1852 when yet more petitions were sent to Parliament protesting about the state of agriculture. It is not clear why the Association folded but we can hypothesise as to the reasons.

In 1848 the Corn Laws had been repealed so it could be that the members of the association that had been set up primarily to protect these laws felt the game was over. But other associations such as at Hadleigh soldiered on. It may be that the Essex Agricultural Society which was formed in 1859 and held the first Essex show that year took some of THAAs energy away, but the years don't really add up. You could also argue that the THAA didn't really die out but rather, it lay dormant for fifty years until Messrs Eagle and Wenden revived it. Indeed when Eagle and Wenden deliberated where to hold the first Tendring Show they chose to return to the place where the THAA held their shows fifty years previous - that being Thorpe Hall.

A cattle show in the 1840s.

THE BRITISH FARMER

OLD BREED   NEW BREED

THE ROYAL AGRICULTURAL EXHIBITION.
Specimens which ought to be included in the Show.
"Prosperity," by Management, out of Better Times. | "Adversity," by Foreign Competition, out of Hard Times.

A cartoon from Punch magazine illustrating how the Victorian era was a time of contrasting fortunes for British farmers. This often inspired the creation of local Farmers Clubs as farmers recognised the need to combine and to organise.

At the luncheon of that first show in 1899 some very old men vaguely recollected something similar being held before. If you look at the names of those who sat down to lunch both in 1840s and in 1899 there are clear family connections. Amongst those farming families present at both occasions were the Blyths of St. Osyth, the Pertwees of Manningtree, the Coopers of Gt. Oakley, the Smiths of Great Clacton, the Giles of Little Holland, the Fenns of Ardleigh, the Brooks of Mistley, the Wendens of Frating, the Salmons of Beaumont, the Lowes of Gt. Holland, the Welhams of Little Clacton and finally the Thompsons of Thorpe. The Thompsons merit special mention in this book because throughout the nineteenth century the family were the tenants of Thorpe Hall and so it was thanks to them a venue was provided both in the 1840s and in 1899. Today Thorpe Hall is a Spa Hotel, a sign of the great changes the area has seen over the years. But the good news is most of the families named above have not disappeared.

Despite these clear links between the Shows of the 1840s and their revival fifty years later, there is no doubt the Tendring Hundred Farmers Club founded in 1899 was a new venture as indeed was the first show. And so, primarily for this reason and partly because it would mess up the title of this book, we are starting the count of Tendring Shows in 1899 not in 1832.

🌿

Chapter Two

THE EARLY YEARS

Before we discuss the first shows we should briefly mention what had happened to the Tendring Hundred in the second half of the nineteenth century because it partly explains why the Shows in the 1900s were significantly different to the exhibitions held fifty years previously. In short, in these intervening years, the Tendring Hundred was fundamentally changed by transport and tourism.

As the THHA show was dying out in the late 1840s a very new and very different form of entertainment was springing up on the beaches and cliffs to the south of the village of Great Clacton and further up the coast at Walton. As was the emerging fashion in Victorian England, the inhabitants of the rapidly expanding city of London were starting to regularly visit the sea-side to escape the foul air and general filth of the crowded metropolis. The newly invented steamer boats could transport thousands down the Thames and deposit them on the beaches along the Essex and Kent coast. In response, the locals built piers, hotels and places of entertainment

The cliffs at Walton in 1883 with the Railway Terminus building in the background and John Eagle's cows in the foreground.

or refreshment to lure in the day-tripping Londoners with their money. In essence, this is how two completely new towns, Clacton-on-Sea and Walton-on-the-Naze sprang up and multiplied from 1850 onwards to quickly become the Tendring Hundred's main centres of population. The district was rapidly moving from being a rural place where the main employment was agriculture to one that was becoming increasingly urban and more diverse in terms of industry and occupation.

Additionally, and partly in response to this, the railways arrived in North East Essex in the 1870s with the terminus at Clacton being opened in 1882. The Tendring Hundred was no longer as remote as it had been from the millions who lived in London. Indeed London itself was building out into the County of Essex. In Georgian times East and West Ham were rural Essex villages; by 1900 they were a contiguous part of the east-end of London. At the other end of the County, Clacton, Walton and Harwich were now just a couple of hours away by train from the world's largest city. Indeed the railway has a part to play in the story of the first Tendring Show. It's no coincidence that Eagle and Wenden decided to hold the first show a few hundred yards from the not long opened railway station at Thorpe-Le-Soken. They even negotiated a deal with the Great Eastern Railway Co. whereby for discounted tickets of 6d showgoers could travel from far away places such as Chelmsford, Maldon and Ipswich to Thorpe for the day. It should be remembered that Railway

Companies in these times were keen to sponsor and promote exhibitions and events in order to encourage people to travel on their railways.

So let's now shift to the inaugural date of Thursday 13th July 1899, the day of the first Tendring Show. Just as would always be the case in the future, the most important factor in the success of the first show was the weather. It did not let them down. The sunny dry weather was described as being 'everything that could be desired'. Inevitably some moaned about it being 'too tropical'. It should be remembered that the late Victorians dressed themselves in many layers of thick material, not forgetting hats, all of which made walking around uncomfortably hot even in mild July weather.

A map of Thorpe Le Soken and Thorpe Hall in 1899 when it provided the first venue for the Tendring Show.

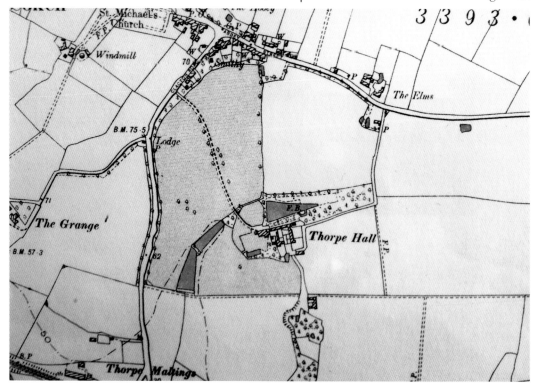

The village of Thorpe-Le-Soken seemed to revel in hosting the first show with bunting strewn across the High Street adding to the gaiety of the day. More widely a 'holiday atmosphere' was reported across the district with work being suspended. A large arch made from greenery was erected at the corner of Clacton Road where visitors coming from the direction of the High Street would have joined those coming up from the Station. On one side of the arch was written in large letters 'Welcome One and All' while on the other side was 'God Save the Queen'. At the entrance a booth was constructed where show goers were charged one shilling for a full day or 6d if they arrived after 2 p.m. Inside the ground there were two rings; one for horse jumping and the other for showing stock. There was a total fund of £150 for prizes for several competitions for horses, cows, pigs and sheep. Appropriately, John Eagle's prize Suffolk Ram, 'Gunner 11' took a red rosette with the judge commenting that 'this was an animal that would win prizes anywhere and in any country'. There were stalls selling farm machinery such as binders, carts and elevators as well as more general goods such as bikes. Joslins, the well regarded Colchester Ironmongers, had a stand. Most importantly there was a beer tent with a Mr. Potton from the Swan Inn in Colchester providing what must have been welcome refreshment on a hot day. There was also entertainment in the form of the band of the Royal Irish Fusiliers from Colchester.

MUTTON

In keeping with the format from the Shows fifty years previous, a large luncheon marquee was erected where about two hundred members sat down for lunch. After the meal, just as fifty years before, 'the cloth was removed' and the speeches were begun. First up was the President of the Club who in that inaugural year was Colonel J.P. Davis of Walton. Davis was an ex Indian-Army man who had bought New House Farm in Walton in 1890 and in retirement had become a Justice of the Peace. As the first President of the Show he has a little place in history. In his speech he acknowledged the work of John Eagle in founding THFC. Finally he toasted the Tendring Show's future success wishing for many shows to be held in the future. They proved portentous words.

A GALLOWAY.

GIVING "DANESFIELD CHALLENGER" A PARTING.

JUDGES
(UNOFFICIAL)

The first general meeting of the Tendring Hundred Farmers Club was held at the Bell Inn, Thorpe-Le-Soken on 15th November 1899. Forty eight of the Club's pioneering members sat down for 'a capital meat tea'. They were joined by the local Vicar, the reverend G.W. Tucker and James Round the local MP for Harwich who took the Chair. In his address Round made mention of the clubs 'courteous and indefatigable' secretary Ernest Wenden and thanked him for his hard work in putting the Show together. In this, we are reminded that at the time the club needed committed hard working people like Wenden. Most importantly a profit of £69 on the clubs first year of activity was declared with gate money at the Show of £93 and subscriptions at £165. From this we can deduce the attendance was in the region of 2,500. Throughout its early years the Show seemed to average this size of gate, with the attendance mainly composed of farmers, farm labourers and a smattering of land owning gentry and other local dignitaries.

At the first meeting it was emphatically agreed that the annual show should continue with the next being held at Mistley Place on the southern banks of the Stour Estuary. Again it was to be in walking distance of a railway station. It is worth remembering at this point that before the 1950s it was traditional for agricultural shows to be peripatetic - moving to different sites every year without putting down roots at one Showground. This was especially true of the bigger shows - indeed the

Essex County Show had been held at Mistley Place in 1885 and in 1900 it came to Clacton. We don't know exactly why the organisers of the Essex Show chose to come to Clacton the very year after the first Tendring Show just five miles away but it does seem a little mischievous. The irony for Tendring farmers was that after years of having no locally held agricultural show to attend, suddenly in 1900 they had two!

The nations leading Show, the now firmly established Royal Show, also moved around the country. In 1899 it was in Maidstone in Kent while in 1900 it was at York. Similarly the farmers of Tendring showed no interest in having a permanent home for their show and it wasn't until after the Second World War that the Show didn't up sticks and move every year. One consequence of this gypsy policy was that in the early years the Show was dependent on the generosity of different landowners and their tenant farmers to host the Show without charge. The usual form was to select a President who had grounds and parkland suitable for holding a show. At one of the early AGMs Eagle described this as selecting a gentlemen from the area and 'bleeding them as best they could'.

Mistley Place was the family home of the Norman family and C. K. Norman was chosen as the Club's second annual President. He was also the master of the local hunt. There was always to be a strong connection between the club and the local hunt which survives to this

day. The Show was held on 25th July and in terms of format now seemed set on a familiar layout with two rings, stock competitions (with prizes amounting to £216), machinery stands, a marching band (costing £11 11s 2d) and various refreshment tents with a luncheon for Vice Presidents and guests of the President in the afternoon. Again at the lunch, speeches were made in praise of farming and the Show. In the speeches there was a mixture of the humorous and the earnest. We should remember in 1900 Britain was at war in South Africa against the Boers. Just as they had done sixty years ago, those giving speeches railed against the foolishness of importing significant amounts of the nations food needs - especially from places like South Africa.

At the Mistley Show there was an unfortunate incident when a horse in the jumping competition shied at the water jump and jumped the outer ring fence into the crowd. A spectator, Mr. Taylor from Bradfield, was knocked to the ground and was rendered unconscious. Chief Inspector Burrell of Mistley Police summoned Dr. Baxter from the Vice President's enclosure who duly attended to Mr. Taylor, who subsequently recovered to the point he could make his way home. Clearly showgoers were made of tough stuff in these days. But such incidents did not mire the Show with the Club going from strength to strength. It now had 300 members paying subs and gate money was up at £95 4s.

In 1901 the Show returned to Thorpe but

this time was held in the grounds of Thorpe's most notable house - Comarques. Again, a Thursday in mid July (the 18th) was chosen as the date. It wasn't until the 1940s after the advent of the notion of the two day weekend in the 1930s that show day shifted to a Saturday. In Edwardian times, before the five day, forty hour working week was established, there was no difference between a Thursday and a Saturday. As to why the timing of mid July was chosen - it can only be assumed. June and July were the favoured months for agricultural shows because of the summer weather. Mid July would have been a convenient time between hay making and the start of harvest for Tendring farmers.

James Round Esquire. Long standing MP for East Essex and early supporter of the fledgling Tendring Hundred Farmers Club. Show President in 1903.

The President in 1901 was James Round. Round had been a local MP since 1868. The Rounds were part of the Tory squirearchy of North East Essex and can be found attending the earlier THAA shows in the 1830s. Throughout the nineteenth century the family members had held the East Essex parliamentary constituency which returned two MPs until it was reorganised in 1885 with James becoming the MP for the Harwich constituency - which was essentially the Tendring Hundred. Round never lost an election but when he stood down from politics in the 1906 election the seat was won by the Liberals. Throughout the twentieth century the voters of the Tendring Hundred showed no great allegiance to any particular party with the seat regularly swinging from the Tories to various others.

The Fourth Earl of Onslow Governor General of New Zealand, President of the Board of Trade for Agriculture and The Sixth President of the Tendring Show.

In these early days the newly formed Tendring Hundred Farmers Club would have needed friends in high places and the Rounds were just that. Another such was the Earl of Onslow who, like James Round, was a Vice President of the Show from 1899 onwards. The Onslows originated from Shropshire but by Victorian times owned vast tracts of farmland in a number of counties - largely due to marriage with the Hillier family. More locally they owned farms in Thorpe, Weeley and St. Osyth. The fourth Earl was William Hillier Onslow who was born in 1853 and died in 1911. The Onslows were a political family going back to the Reformation Royal Court of the 1670s. As a good 'chip off the old block', William held positions at the top of Government including Under Secretary for the Colonies, Governor of New Zealand and most pertinently for this story, he was President of the Board of Trade for Agriculture from 1903 to 1905. As such he was in effect the Minister of Agriculture before that title was invented after the First World War. As a little minor note of trivia it could be noted that he was the last cabinet member to sport a full beard. The fourth Earl Onslow was invited to speak at the 1904 show held at Ballast Quay at Wivenhoe but cancelled at the last minute due to a pressing Parliamentary engagement. However, in 1905 when the Show returned to Thorpe Hall, he was Show President and duly turned up to make a widely reported speech that appeared in the national press. This wide publicity was quite a 'feather in the cap' for what was essentially a very modest local show.

In his speech the Earl acknowledged that the economics of farming at the time were not easy but he urged farmers to breed the best stock if they wished to succeed. This was apt because Onslow himself was a devoted breeder of Black pigs and had shown his pigs at all the early Tendring Shows, always winning first prize. In all of this we are reminded of the P.G. Wodehouse character 'Lord Emsworth' who some think was in part inspired by the fourth Earl Onslow. In Wodehouse's comedic novels about the eccentric aristocratic family who lived in Blandings Castle, Lord Emsworth doted hilariously, but touchingly, on his prize winning Black Berkshire sow called 'The Empress of Blandings' which won prizes at the Shropshire County Show. This, in turn, is a reminder that many of the Victorian and Edwardian British Aristocracy took personal pride in owning prize winning livestock while lavishing both time and money in pursuit of silverware at the more prestigious County and Royal Shows. This did not always please the more average 'commercial' farmers who could not afford such indulgence.

BERKSHIRES

John Eagle was one such and he expressed the view at the Luncheon of the 1902 show at Ardleigh that one of great virtues of smaller local shows was that they gave ordinary farmers the opportunity to show off their stock which, in turn, encouraged improvement in better breeding amongst commercial farmers. Eagle went on to criticise stock competitions at the County Show level where they were dominated by the 'well heeled gentleman hobbyists and pot-hunters'. History does not record what Eagle thought of the Earl of Onslow and his over-pampered prize winning Black pigs that swept the boards at his local show that Eagle spent so much time in putting together. This little episode reminds us that in its early days the Tendring Show had a key role in the improvement of agriculture for local working farmers while also attracting outside interest.

John Eagle's Share Certificate in the short lived Tendring Hundred Co-operative Society set up by the Tendring Hundred Farmers Club.

From its inception it was clear the newly formed Tendring Hundred Farmers Club did

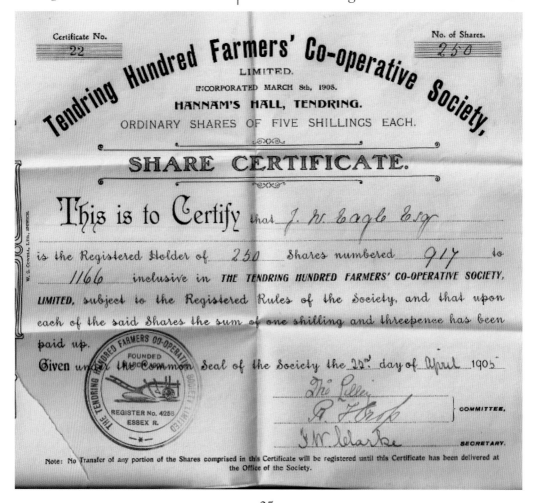

not see itself as just concerned with putting on an annual show. Meetings were held in the winter, usually at the Maids Head in Thorpe to discuss matters affecting agriculture. On 25th January 1901 the club met to take tea and then to discuss the Pure Beer issue. In late Victorian times, as the manufacture of food stuffs became increasingly industrialised brewers started using all sorts of ingredients in their brews other than the traditional malting barley. This infuriated farmers who demanded of Parliament that a law was brought in similar to one in Germany that restricted the ingredients of beer to just water, yeast and barley. As a key malting barley area this would have been an important issue for Tendring Hundred farmers. James Round, the local MP was invited to the meeting and a letter was sent in support of a Parliamentary motion in

The band plays on at Wivenhoe Hall, venue for the 1913 Tendring Show.

support of Pure Beer regulation. Unfortunately for Tendring Farmers, the Brewing lobby proved more effective and the motion was lost. Other issues discussed in winter meetings proved as diverse as: the inadequacies of the Great Eastern Railway; the control of rats; the best model for farm management; the need for a local sugar beet factory and the better breeding of sheep. All good talking points that can still be heard being discussed among Tendring farmers today.

Another issue for debate was that of commercial co-operation between farmers. As farming fortunes faltered around the turn of the twentieth century, new ideas to revive the farming economy became much discussed. One such was farmer co-ops where farmers grouped together to give them more collective bargaining power when it came to buying and selling. At the annual meeting in February 1905 it was resolved that the Club should form the Tendring Hundred Farmers Co-operative

Winner of the best in breed at the 1903 show - the earliest known photo of the Tendring Show.

[ARISIAN] **Tendring Hundred Farmers' Club Show, July, 1903.** [STUDIO.
First and second Prize Winners, property of Gilders Bros.

Society (THFCS). Although it was formed and attracted over sixty members it did not prove a roaring success. This was fairly typical of the many farmer co-ops that started up at this time in the UK. The co-operative model never took root in the UK as it did on the Continent where the vast majority of farmers bought and sold collectively rather than individually. The main reason for this was that farm sizes were larger in the UK which invoked a greater sense of self-reliance and independence among farmers. This would have been true of farmers in the Tendring Hundred where the larger than UK average farm size would have been around 500 acres. THFC Chairman John Eagle had joined the THFCS but it was clear that he was wary of the Club straying from what he saw as its prime aim - namely the encouragement of the better breeding of stock through showing them at the annual show.

The fourth show in 1903 was different to the three previous in that it wasn't held in landscaped parkland but rather on a field near Wash Farm located on the western outskirts of the rapidly expanding new town of Clacton-on-Sea. The President that year was Thomas Lilley. Lilley had made his fortune from the manufacturing and retailing of shoes through his nationally known firm 'Lilley and Skinner' based in Northampton. He had moved to Clacton in his late forties to become a leading light in the local burgeoning sea-side community. This fact is a reminder that in Edwardian times Clacton was seen as highly fashionable with the 'well to do' and attracted

Mr. T. Lilley, J.P.
(President of the Tendring Hundred Farmers' Club).

Thomas Lilley - Clacton dignitary, Shoe Magnate and twice Show President.

the monied classes. At the Show Lilley had his own little 'enclosure' where he entertained the towns 'smart set' to tea. Lilley was a good early example of a President of the Show who wasn't primarily a farmer. Throughout its history the Club has always been happy to occasionally choose individuals from outside of farming ranks to be the President. Lilley remained a great supporter of the Show and was President again in 1908.

The Clacton show was well organised but rather expensive to put on with a 'musical ride' by the 5th Royal Lancers accompanied by the band of the 2nd Royal Norfolk Battalion. They all arrived on a special train from London. Despite the quality of the entertainment the weather refused to perform with three hours of steady rain followed by regular showers. Although the gate was the best yet at £152.3s.2d the general feeling was not as many from Clacton

The Heavy Horse - the power supply for Tendring Farms in the first half of the twentieth century.

had turned out as was hoped. The Show would have lost money if the Royal Lancers had not been paid for by the Clacton Town Council. This meteorological embarrassment for a town that promoted itself as 'sunny Clacton' was repeated when the Show returned in 1908 five years later. On that day the rain was described as 'doggedly persistent'. As the reporter from the Colchester Standard put it 'the Show had good entries and an influential list of patrons but it has to be regretted that Jupiter Pluvius was at the last moment numbered among the latter deputising for Old Sol who was notable by his absence'. The double irony for sunny Clacton was that it hosted the only two pre-First World War shows that weren't blessed with good weather. To compound the problem the 1908 site, near the Convalescent Home on the Holland Road, was on clay soil and soon turned into a quagmire. The 'decorated

A DEXTER HEIFER "DANESFIELD MARJORIE"

FRANK GILLETT

motor car parade' in the main ring had to be cancelled. The reporter at the Show also wryly noted that the only people happy were those running the refreshment tents.

Despite this the Show continued to grow in terms of gate and entries. When the 1907 show was held at Weeley in the charmingly named 'Mustards Meadow' at Hillside farm, a 'Poultry Class' had been added which increased entries considerably. This was despite the fact the Pig classes were cancelled that year due to restrictions brought in by the Board of Trade for Agriculture to combat a local Swine Fever outbreak. There was also a bit of controversy at the Weeley Show when a Mr. Ward objected to the judges awarding Mr. Wenden's horse the best gelding because it was actually 'entire'. The judges refused to budge and allowed Wenden to keep the Cup on the grounds that his animal was the only entry. One wag was noted to comment 'if the Show Committee introduces an Elephant Class next year he will enter his tom-cat in the hope there are no other entries'.

The 1907 show also saw the introduction of a sheep-shearing competition. At the 1910 show at Thorpe, a Horticultural section was added which included flowers, needlework and home industries. Now for the first time women were winning prizes at the Show. On the down side it was noted that at the 1911 show at Ardleigh the number of 'light horses' being entered was starting to fall and this was blamed on the increasing popularity of the motor car as a preferred mode of transport. In contrast, the tractor was yet to appear on Tendring farms, so accordingly the 'heavy horse' classes remained in good health. The demise of the heavy horse as an agricultural power-house in the face of the internal combustion engine was still to come. Even so, there was no shortage of new mechanical innovations displayed at these early shows. At the 1911 Ardleigh Show, Brittains of Chelmsford displayed the new Massey Harris horse drawn binder. More locally the Canhams of Weeley could be found at most of the Shows showing off their new American style light-weight carts. The Williams Company were also regulars at the Show selling machinery.

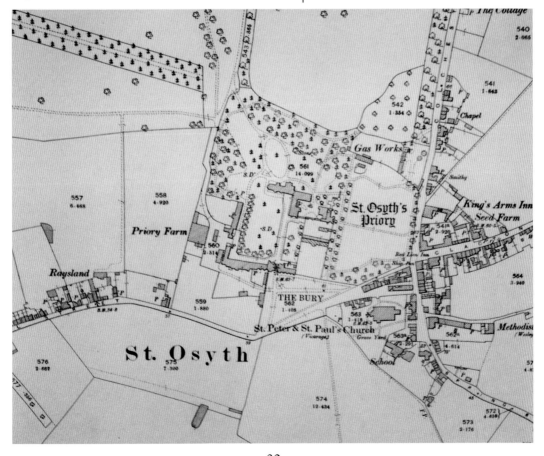

The increasing appearance of motor cars on the roads of the Tendring Hundred was probably one reason why the club chose to hold the 1914 show at St. Osyth Priory. St. Osyth was the District's largest village not to have a railway link. Before 1914 all shows had been held within a few hundred yards of a station.

The St. Osyth show was also a notable first in as much that it had a female President in the form of Lady Cowley, the owner of the Priory Estate. In 1914 the choice of a woman for such a role was ground breaking and it was reported widely in the national press. It even made the front page of the Liverpool Echo. We should remember here that this was the era of the suffragettes when the position of women in society was a much discussed and contentious issue. Whether the Tendring Hundred Farmers Club saw themselves as some sort of

A PROUD MOMENT. FIXING ON HIS ROSETTE.

proto-feminist trailblazers is another matter. It might also be doubted whether Lady Cowley saw herself as much of a poster girl for the Suffragette cause. At the Show Luncheon she chose not to speak but rather her husband, Dr. Cowley, gave the President's address on her behalf.

Another novel idea at the 1914 show was to combine it with the St. Osyth Horticultural Society show. The display of Sweet Peas was particularly noteworthy. The fact that the Priory grounds and gardens were also open must have added to the event. As indeed did the exotically entitled 'Xylonite Works Band' who performed throughout the day. Xylonite was an early form of plastic made at a large factory near Brantham where the band hailed from. There was also a strong army presence

at St. Osyth with the 20th Hussars displaying musical rides, vaulting, gymnastic exhibitions, tent pegging and 'a Balaclava melee'. Within five weeks these same soldiers and horses would find themselves in far less salubrious surroundings on the Western Front. The 20th Hussars were involved in the first cavalry action of the First World War but soon became entrenched with the rest of the British army in the brutal four year stand-off. But at the 1914 Tendring Show that was yet to come and no significant shadow was cast over the day. As the record crowd of four thousand enjoyed the pleasant summer weather wandering around the convivial entertainment amidst the beautiful grounds of St. Osyth Priory, you can only assume no one was unduly downcast about the prospect of the horrors that were about to unravel across continental Europe when war was declared just twelve days later. The Great War was to prove to be one of the grimmest episodes in British history that left no British family untouched and disturbed for the worse many aspects of daily life - including the holding of agricultural shows.

So we come to the end of this early chapter in the story of the Tendring Show. We have reached show number sixteen as we count towards one hundred. It wasn't until 1919 that the seventeenth was held.

Chapter Three

INTERWAR STRUGGLES

When the Show reconvened on Wednesday 20th July 1919 after four years of cancellations due to the hostilities, it seemed wholly appropriate it should return to its favourite stamping ground at Thorpe Hall. It was all the more fitting because the Hall was now the home of a hero of the Great War - General Sir Julian Byng. Byng was a career soldier who had bought Thorpe Hall in 1913 where his wife set about transforming the gardens. Meanwhile on the Western Front Byng masterminded one of the British Army's most famous victories - the capture of the Vimy Ridge in 1917. Following this success he was put in charge of the Third Army at Cambrai which saw the introduction of the tank as a tool of modern warfare. After the war Byng was showered with honours and raised to the Peerage as Baron Byng of Vimy.

So, not for the first time, the Tendring Show managed to attract one of the nation's most famous men as its President. The 1919 Show was known as a 'Victory Show'. The afternoon saw the arrival in the main ring of what must

Lord Byng and his war time pal - Prince Arthur of Connaught who paid a 'short but interested visit' to the 1928 show.

have been one of the most startling sites ever to appear at a Tendring Show - a C3 Tank, which navigated the water jump with consummate ease. The tank arrived by permission of the War Office but no doubt Byng pulled strings to make it happen. The crowd must have been filled with a sense of wonder and awe if not a little trepidation. Similar to the previous show at St. Osyth four years previously the local Thorpe Garden Show was incorporated into the event and thus helped secure another large crowd. It seemed the Show was back to form and hadn't suffered from the war-time intermission in the way other shows had. Generally there was a bit of optimism in the local farming community as the war had reminded Government and townsfolk alike of the importance of agriculture. The German U-boat blockade had started to cause serious problems with Britain's food supplies in 1916-17. This not only raised farm-gate prices but reintroduced the plough to many hundreds

of acres of Tendring farmland that had lain derelict for as long as some could remember. Lord Byng, in his luncheon speech, spoke of a 'smiling time for agriculture'. On that sunny day in the grounds of Thorpe Hall the crowds had much to smile about after four long years of misery.

In 1921 the Show returned to Clacton and for once 'sunny Clacton' shined on the event. Whether the hot show weather pleased the farmers is not clear as the area was in the grip of a prolonged drought at the time. The poor growing conditions reflected in the horticultural classes. The venue was Tower field, pleasantly located next to the sea front adjoining the newly laid out town golf course on the western edge of the town. It took its name from the presence of an old Martello defence tower built near the beach during the Napoleonic wars one hundred years previous. The land was owned by the Smith family. The Smiths were a long established farming family who had farmed land between Clacton and St. Osyth since Tudor times. By the late nineteenth century they were forerunners of the increasing trend in the twentieth century for farmers to own the land they farmed rather than rent it from the gentry. By the 1920s the Smiths owned several hundred acres which fifty years before had been part of the huge St. Osyth Priory Estate which had covered some 4000 acres across twenty farms. At this time many of the old landed estates, such as that owned by the Onslows, were being disbanded under pressure from recently introduced death duties

John Smith on Tower field Clacton - venue for the 1921 show and ninety five years later how the same scene looks today with John Smith's great-great Granddaughters, Elizabeth and Emelia, in shot.

made worse by another down turn in farming economics in the early 1920s. It is reckoned that more English land changed hands in the 1920s than at any other time in English history since the Norman conquest. Slowly but surely farms and indeed Tendring Show venues, were increasingly farmed by owner occupiers such as the Smiths.

The 1921 Show at Clacton was considered one of the best to date but worryingly it lost a thumping £148. It was concluded at the following AGM that the sort of people who visited sea-side resorts were not really interested in agriculture. 1921 was the third and last time the Show visited Clacton. Tower field was soon to be bought by Mr. Billy Butlin where he built an enormous holiday camp. The old Martello tower was used to house the camps water supply.

A prize winning Friesian Bull at the 1932 Show. In between the wars the Friesian replaced the short-horn as the dairy cow of choice in the Tendring Hundred.

One new feature in the Shows of the 1920s was long service awards for farm labourers. At the 1926 Show at Michaelstowe Hall in Ramsey, an award was given to 84 year old Joseph Davis who worked on Gurnhams Farm, Little Bentley. Incredibly, Davis had clocked up seventy seven years as a horseman on the same farm having started there at the age of seven. On receiving his award amidst a large round of applause he announced he thought the award a little premature as he had no plans to retire! What he thought about the tractors that were starting to appear on some of the machinery stands was not recorded. The fact was that the days of the horsemen were numbered and the Tendring show was starting to reflect

Recipients of long service awards at the 1926 Show including the redoubtable Joseph Davis, shown below on the right, who had clocked up seventy seven years of employment on Gurnhams Farm, Little Bentley.

that. Such technical progress was not always approved of. At the luncheon at the Ramsey show, a Captain Campbell in his speech on behalf of the guests and judges loudly lamented the fact that 'nowadays farmers boys ride those blasted motorcycles'. He suggested all farmers should give these boys a good young horse as this would 'save the boy and save the farm and also save peoples ears'. He added that his advice to arable farmers was to forget current low prices and to buy a hunter and 'hunt for as long as the bankers would afford you it'. But this change in farm transport wasn't all bad news for the Show as manifested by the fact that the Anglo-American Oil Company were now regular and enthusiastic stand holders. The 1926 venue Michaelstowe Hall was a large house located in magnificent gardens on the

An exhibition of Hounds at the 1932 show.

More long service awards at the 1927 Show.

TENDRING HUNDRED FARMERS' CLUB

President: R. C. ABDY, Esq.

THE
ANNUAL SHOW

WILL BE HELD AT

MICHAELSTOWE HALL,
DOVERCOURT

BY KIND PERMISSION OF THE PRESIDENT

On WEDNESDAY, JULY 14, 1926

Prizes to the value of £600

Including 7 Silver Challenge Cups and Medals

Shires, Suffolk Horses, Hunters. Hackneys. Neat Stock, Friesians. Sheep and Pigs.

Decorative and Garden Produce Section. Flowers. Fruit and Vegetables.

2 JUMPING COMPETITIONS
OPEN TO ALL COMERS

Judging by Farmers' Sons. The Best Turn-out Driven by a Lady.

LONG SERVICE CLASS FOR WORKMEN. Prizes £3 3s., £2 2s. and £1 1s.

ENTRIES CLOSE JUNE 26th, 1926.

HARWICH SILVER BAND WILL BE IN ATTENDANCE

Buses will run to the Show from all Parts

PUBLIC LUNCHEON
Supplied by Messrs. Tweed & Son, North Station Road, Colchester. TICKETS 4s. 6d. each.

Show Opens at **10** o'clock **Admission 2s. After 2 p.m. 1s.**

GOOD ACCOMMODATION FOR MOTOR CARS AND CYCLES.

For schedules and full particulars apply: HERBERT E WENDEN, Secretary. LOWER FARM, LAWFORD.

outskirts of Harwich. It was owned by Richard Adby who had made his fortune in banking, most notably as Chairman of the Bank of Egypt. He employed sixty gardeners and must have kept show-goers amused by offering a pound to anyone who could find a weed. The Show returned to Michaelstowe Hall in 1931 where the convivial Mr Adby hosted the Show again as President. It proved Mr Adby's last hurrah at Michaelstowe as the banking crash of the early 1930s straitened his circumstances forcing him to sell the place in 1932.

The 1927 show returned yet again to Thorpe Hall again by courtesy of the Byngs. Lord Byng had recently returned from Canada having served as Governor General there since 1921. It is a striking coincidence in that with Lord Byng and Lord Onslow the Club had two Presidents in its early years who had been

R.C. Abdy President of the 1926 and 1931 Shows held in his immaculate grounds at Michaelstowe Hall.

at Michaelstowe Hall, Ramsey.

Photographs by J. E. Stalter, Colchester.

Governor Generals of significant parts of the Empire. Such friends in high places yielded a real show stopper in 1928 when a member of the Royal Family, Prince Arthur of Connaught, turned up unannounced for a 'short but interested' look round the Show which that year was at Gt. Bromley Hall. Prince Arthur was an old acquaintance with Lord Byng from their army days. Despite the Royal appearance the 1928 Show lost money - £1.4s.8d to be precise. The low gate was not helped by wet weather in the early morning when people were deciding whether to attend.

Unfortunately for the club these losses were indicative of cracks that were starting to appear in the late 1920s. The reasons seem manifold. Some shows were cursed with bad weather while others, such as the 1926 show,

TENDRING HUNDRED SHOW AT MISTLEY .

TENDRING HUNDRED FARMERS' CLUB SHOW AT MISTLEY

Photographs by J. E. Stutter.

COMPETITORS IN YOUNG CALF CLUBS' CLASS.—Names (left to right): ——, Margaret McBain (Little Clacton), Jessie Macdonald (Great Bentley), Jessie Lord (Great Bentley), Clifford Halsel (Langham), T. Miller (Frating Abbey), Maurice Clarey (Tendring), Geo. Miller (Frating Abbey), —— Lord (Tendring).

were depleted through animal movement restrictions because of disease such as Foot and Mouth. The 1926 Show was the only pre-war show to have no cattle making an appearance. Crowd pulling events such as the British Empire exhibition at Wembley and large military tattoos in Colchester also didn't help. But more generally, the demise in the club can be linked to a demise in the fortunes of farming. The late twenties and early thirties were very tough times for agriculture with farm-gate prices at all time lows. The depression hit arable areas in the east harder than the more livestock orientated west. Many Tendring farm tenants were walking away from their farms while landlords were offering farms rent free in order to stop them from becoming derelict. Meanwhile the owner-occupiers were frequently filing for bankruptcy. Even livestock numbers declined and several local well regarded sheep flocks were disbanded. This

The NFU Tent, a regular at the Tendring show from the 1920s onwards.

Above: Mrs Phoebe Bond showing her prize winning cow at the 1923 Show at St.Osyth.

all ate into the well-being of the club. There were fewer farmers and those that were left had less time and money to spend on the Show.

At the 1927 AGM concerns were expressed that younger men were not coming forward to take on roles in the club. Two thirds of the committee in 1900 were still there twenty five years later while some stalwarts such as John Eagle had passed away. The irony was that since the earliest shows, the annual event had grown with new classes and new attractions making it more expensive to put on. So although it was growing, it was at the same time becoming very vulnerable to low income from low gates caused by circumstances out of the Club's control.

Frequently the Club was financially dependent on benevolent gestures. This was the case in 1930. The Show that year returned to Comarques in Thorpe that was now the home of Lord Fairfax. Although he was an American by birth, the fourth Earl came from a long line of landed aristocrats. Indeed, his most famous ancestor, Thomas Fairfax, was Lord General of the Parliamentary forces in the Civil War and led the siege of Colchester. In the eighteenth century the Fairfax family had moved to America where they laid claim to vast tracts of Virginia but in the early twentieth century they returned to Britain to revive the family title. They chose Comarques in Thorpe as the new family seat. Such patronage was useful because it not only provided a charming venue for the Show but also Lord Fairfax dipped into his own pockets when the Show he was

Lord Fairfax - host and President of the 1930 Show at Thorpe. He also covered the Show's losses of £19 10s.

Suffolk sheep being judged at the 1932 Show.

President of lost £19. 10s. Again, wet weather seems to have spoilt the attendance. It would seem Fairfax was not immune to loss making ventures. In his speech he described farming as 'not so much a business, more an extravagant luxury'.

In 1934 the Show was cancelled due to the rival attraction at Ipswich of the Royal Show, complete with the star-billing of the Prince of Wales, before his fall from grace two years later as the abdicated Edward VIII.

After another disappointing show in 1931 at Ramsey there was an additional problem for the Show Committee. The 1932 Essex County Show was scheduled to be held in nearby Colchester. Fearful that this would damage both gate and entries, the Club approached the Essex Agricultural Society with the suggestion that there was a merger with thirty of the Club's competitions to be held at the

JULY 9, 1934.   THE FARMER AND STOCK-BREEDER.   1579

A Great Royal Show

FOR the second time in its history the Royal Agricultural Society of England last week held its show in Suffolk. The first occasion was in 1867, when it visited Bury St. Edmunds, and this year for the first time Ipswich has been the Society's host. In 1867 the total number of entries of live stock was 719, but at Ipswich the number reached 3,554. Of this latter figure breeds identified with East Anglia—Suffolk horses, Red Poll cattle, Suffolk sheep, and Essex pigs—supplied 715.

The show opened on Tuesday, and on the second day the Prince of Wales paid it a visit. His Royal Highness arrived at the Royal Pavilion at noon and was received by the president, the Earl of Stradbroke. He had previously been welcomed by the Mayor of Ipswich (Mr. P. W. Cobbold) at the borough boundary. In the afternoon he made a tour of the showyard, inspecting many of the features, and watched some judging and the parade of Suffolk horses from the grandstand. This was a solo parade, in which no other breed participated, but in which every Suffolk exhibit took part. The distinction was a well-deserved compliment to the breed that provided the largest entry in the show, and much the largest it has ever made in any showyard.

The Ipswich Royal Show was built on a good foundation. It can with confidence be stated that never has the exhibition been held on a better showground; if it has been held on one as good it must have been more than thirty-seven years ago. From corner to corner diagonally it did not exceed half a mile, and in addition to being compact with no dead country, it was wonderfully well laid out. As has been mentioned

H.R.H. the Prince of Wales motored to the Royal Show on Wednesday and spent the afternoon in a tour of the main features of interest. A great crowd cheered the Prince with enthusiasm.—Photograph by Sport and General.

than last year, totalled 136. Southdowns, with 82 pens, came next to the local breed in the Sheep section, and it was only in the Pig section that the locals were beaten in number. Large

Tuesday. The day opened bright and warm, and at one time it appeared as if it might become oppressively hot, but a breeze sprang up later on which tended to keep the conditions

County show as well as the Club running the Horticultural Section. This was agreed and a successful show was held over two days in mid June at a large showground at Middlewick.

The following year in 1933 a show was held at Park Lodge Meadow, Mistley and again it lost money. Despite a reasonably healthy crowd of around 4000, an £80 loss was recorded. To compound problems, the following year in 1934 the club faced yet another 'rival show dilemma' but this time it was the biggest of all Shows that had appeared on a near horizon - the Royal Show was scheduled to be held at Ipswich in July.

TENDRING HUNDRED
FARMERS' CLUB.

President :

W. HILTON H. BROOKS, Esq., J.P.

ANNUAL SHOW.

OFFICIAL
CATALOGUE

PARK LODGE MEADOW,
MISTLEY

(By kind permission of the President),

WEDNESDAY, JULY 12th, 1933.

Benham & Company Limited, Printers, Colchester.

Tendring Hundred Farmers' Club.

OFFICERS FOR THE YEAR 1933.

President: W. HILTON H. BROOKS, Esq., J.P.

Vice-Presidents:

Brig.-Gen. R. ATKINSON, C.B., C.M.G., Major-Gen. R. L. MULLENS, C.B.
Brig.-Gen. K. J. KINCAID-SMITH, C.B., C.M.G., D.S.O., J.P.

ABBOTT, E., Esq.
ALSTON, A. E., Esq.
BAKER, M., Esq., J.P.
BALL, J. E., Esq.
BARKER, F., Esq.
BENHAM, W. GURNEY, Esq., J.P.
BLEWITT, Lt.-Col. GUY.
BLYTH, J. S., Esq.
BOATMAN, W., Esq.
BREME, —, Esq.
BROOK, L. C., Esq.
BROOKS, C. A., Esq.
BROOKS, W. H. H., Esq., J.P.
BROWN, A. H., Esq.
CLARKE, F. W., Esq.
COBBOLD, G. F., Esq.
COOPER, Sir RICHARD A., Bart.
CROSSMAN, Mrs.
DANIELS, C. N., Esq.
DAWNAY, Mrs. D.
DAWNAY, N. W., Esq.
DIGBY, E. AYLMER, Esq.
DUNNETT, W. H., Esq.
EVANSON, Major E. V. F.
FAIRFAX, Lord.
FENN, J., Esq.
GIBBON, C. H., Esq.
GIBBON, Mrs. C. H.
GILES, E., Esq.
GODDARD, A., Esq.
GRIMWADE, F., Esq.
HALL, Capt. R. S.
HARRIS, Colonel H. J.
HEMPSON, G., Esq.
HILLARY, A., Esq., J.P.
HINES, H. J., Esq.
HUGHES, W. A., Esq.

JONES, S. V. D. DOUGLAS, Esq.
KEEBLE, E. J., Esq., J.P.
Le MOTTEE, Brig.-Gen. R. E. A.
LILLEY, H., Esq.
MANGLES, Lt.-Col. C. G., M.C., M.F.H
MARKHAM, H., Esq.
MASON, J. B., Esq.
MITCHELL, G. K., Esq., J.P.
MOY, E. J., Esq.
MYERS, G. E., Esq.
MUNNINGS, A. J., Esq., R.A.
NICHOLL, P. H., Esq.
NORMAN, E. B. K., Esq., J.P.
PAWSEY, H., Esq.
PYBUS, P. J., Esq., C.B.E., M.P.
RICE, Sir FREDERICK.
RICHARDSON, S., Esq.
ROWLAND, T. R., Esq.
SIMSON, G., Esq.
SMITH, Capt. D. S.
SMITH, W. R., Esq.
SMITH, O. THOMPSON, Esq.
SORRELL, L. B., Esq.
SPOONER, S., Esq.
STANFORD, G., Esq.
SWIFT, G. H. J., Esq.
THEOBALD, Col. A. C. L.
TUFNELL, Major N. A. C. de H., J.P
WARD, Col. A. J. H.
WARNER, R., Esq.
WEBB, W., Esq.
WESTMACOTT, T. H., Esq., O.B.E.
WYATT, J. M. A., Esq.
WAGSTAFF, F. W., Esq.
WALLER, Major A. J. R.
WIGGIN, E., Esq.

Committee:

Mr. S. S. ARMSTRONG.
Mr. A. A. BAGLEY.
Mr. M. BAKER, J.P.
Mr. J. S. BLYTH.
Lt.-Col. GUY BLEWITT.
Mr. A. H. BROWN.
Mr. C. A. BROOKS.
Mr. W. BOATMAN.
Mr. L. CHAMPNESS.
Mr. F. W. CLARKE.
Mr. F. V. CRISP.
Mr. D. P. CROSSMAN.

Mr. R. S. DAKING.
Mr. W. R. DAWNAY.
Mr. J. FENN.
Mr. J. R. M. FITCH.
Mr. E. GILES.
Mr. F. D. GIRLING.
Mr. T. GIRLING.
Mr. F. A. GIRLING.
Mr. A. GODDARD.
Mr. F. GRIMWADE.
Mr. W. H. HARVEY.
Mr. H. C. HAYWARD.

Mr. E. J. KEEBLE, J.P.
Mr. H. LILLEY.
Mr. W. J. LORD.
Mr. J. W. LORD.
Mr. J. B. MASON.
Mr. W. N. PARSONS.
Mr. C. P. ROSE.
Mr. G. STANFORD.
Major A. WALLER.
Mr. W. WEBB.

Treasurer: Major N. A. C. DE H. TUFNELL, J.P.

Chairman: Mr. M. BAKER, J.P.

Secretary: HERBERT E. WENDEN, Rest Nook, Lawford, Manningtree.

The Heavy Horse Class at the
1928 Show at Bromley Hall.

At the AGM on 10th February 1934 the issue as to whether to hold a show was much debated. Eventually a vote was taken, 95 votes in favour of cancellation with 50 against. While the close presence of the Royal Show both in terms of location and calendar may have pre-empted the decision to end what could be seen as thirty five years of progress, the underlying reason was the down-turn in farming. In the words of one of those present at the 1934 AGM, local farmers were not 'steady on their feet due to the financial crisis and until the Show schedule was completely reconstructed then it should be cancelled indefinitely'. There was a healthy £800 still in Club funds but it seemed the will to carry on had run out.

Another wider and related development material to our story that is worth noting at this stage was that the farming families of the

Tendring Hundred were changing. An influx of newcomers were starting to add new colour to the agricultural social scene and that colour was predominantly tartan.

As farm profits emaciated many of the existing farming families threw in the towel and walked away from farms. When this happened, landlords were often prepared to let farms for very little in an initial period in the hope this would attract a tenant to keep the farm in good order. This in turn opened up opportunities for others, particularly those who could make do with less. One such breed of farmers were the frugal Scots who were conditioned by the harsher northern climate with its tougher terrain. For such families the

Mrs. Bryan of Little Clacton and her two prize winning cows at the 1929 Show.

Mrs. Bryan, Little Clacton, with her two prize-winning cows.

Tendring Hundred offered better soils and a better climate along with the chance to own land. There is an apocryphal tale that a Scots farmer arrived on a Tendring farm with his three sons in the 1920s. On the first morning he went out to discuss his plans for the future with the nine farmhands who worked on the farm. Having explained that as any Scotsman was worth two Englishmen he announced he would only be needing to retain one of them.

The first clan to arrive were the Mitchells from Linlithgow near Edinburgh at the turn of the century taking farms in the Bradfield area. News seemed to have spread back to the Scottish central belt of the opportunities of empty farms in the fertile Tendring Hundred needing farmers. More families made the journey south to join the diaspora particularly in the late 1920s and early 1930s when the depression in agricultural prices hit record

Mrs T. A. Bond and her Red Poll 'Polly' who she had reared as a sickly calf.

lows. By the 1940s the Robertsons, the Strangs, the Flemings, the Liepers, the Davidsons, the Macaulays, the Faulds, the McNairs, the Clachans, the Youngs, the Fairleys, the MacDonalds, the McBains, the Cullens, the Strachans and more besides had taken farms across the Tendring Hundred. Writing in the 1940s an agricultural commentator observed: 'The Tendring Hundred has been described as the best farmed area in Britain. Whether it is the farmers or the soils and climate that make it so I do not know. Anyone at all familiar with the farming folk of this area will be aware of the Scottish influence. Whether the Scottish came down to the Tendring Hundred and made it what it is or whether they had such good neighbours that they had to follow suit is not an argument I am prepared to enter into here. Certainly the Scottish element had the

Howay the Scots - The Tendring Show in 2005 still celebrating its Scottish influences.

Above: Young farmer Robert Fairley and his well handled calf 'Flossie'.

Below: Henry Fairley (centre), President at the 1996 Show surrounded by a troop of Scottish Country dancers who performed at the Show. Henry Fairley is typical of many Tendring farmers in the way he is very proud of his Scottish roots.

good wisdom to settle down in this particular part of Essex. Anyway the invasion is now complete and the bonds of matrimony have been solemnised many times between the invaders and the natives'.

It may be that this process of flux and change de-stabilised things across the social farming scene of the district, including the successful running of the THFC. As parts of the old guard disappeared and as newcomers acclimatised themselves to their new surroundings it is likely events such as an annual show suffered amidst the disruption. As we shall see, as things settled down after the Second World War, these newcomers were to have an increasing and beneficial influence on the success of the Show, but the man who sparked the post-war revival was from a long line of Tendring farmers and he was called John Fenn.

Chapter Four

POST-WAR REVIVAL

The Fenns were a long established Tendring Hundred family and can be found well represented at the cattle show at Thorpe in the 1840s. They were farmers based in Ardleigh who, in the nineteenth century, branched out into the dark art of land and estate agency. Farm agents were traditionally a breed of men who operated in the shady territory between the gentry and the tenant farmers as representatives for the landed classes. As such they weren't always the most popular of men in the farming community being embroiled in setting rents as well as in eviction and re-letting farms when existing tenants struggled to make things pay. This could involve auctioning off what remained when the old tenant moved out which could lead to rows with the departing party. They also took commission and attracted farming ire when it came to valuing a farm on the introduction of a new tenant or purchaser.

Despite being involved in some of the more challenging moments in farming life, the agent's strength was having a sharp eye when

'Phone : Colchester 3171 (2 lines).   Telegrams: "Fenenright, Colchester."

FENN, WRIGHT & CO.

(John Fenn, F.A.I.   George T. Wright, F.S.I., F.A.I.)

Auctioneers, Valuers,   .   .
Surveyors & Estate Agents,

146, High Street, Colchester

VALUATIONS for Mortgage. Probate and Real Estate, Copyhold Enfranchisements. Tenant Right and Rating, etc.

ANNUAL WOOL SALE IN JUNE.

SALES by Auction and by Private Treaty, of Business Premises. Town and Country Houses. Farms. Land. Furniture. Live and Dead Farming Stock. Poultry. etc.

PROPRIETORS OF
Colchester New Cattle Market

Weekly Sales held each Saturday.

Modern and up-to-date accommodation for the Sale of Cattle, Sheep and Swine, Horses and Dead Stock.

All Fat Cattle sold over a weighbridge fitted with clock face dial without extra charge.

Stock arriving by train previous to day of sale Unloaded, Fed and Watered.

Special Sales arranged throughout the year.

Entries respectfully solicited and should reach the Auctioneers early in each week preceding Sale, in order that they may be advertised.

Agents to the principal Fire, Accident and Life Insurance Offices.

Full particulars of Houses, Farms, Etc., for Sale or to Let sent on application.

The front page of the July 19th 1946 Essex County Standard heralds the revival of the Tendring Show amidst news of bread rationing and land mines on tourist beaches. At a time of continued post-war austerity that characterised the later 1940s, the revival of the Show must have represented a welcome return to some peace time fun.

it came to what was going on across the local farming scene. It was in their interest to make contact with and gain the trust of as many in the farming community as possible. Hence the involvement of land agents proved invaluable when it came to putting on events such as the Tendring Show just as it still does today.

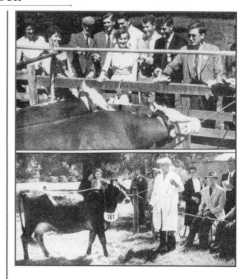

Consequently it is not surprising to find John Fenn chewing the fat with farmers in the summer of 1944 as to how they might help the war effort, in particular how they might raise money for the Red Cross Agriculture Fund. The idea initially was to hold a large fête cum gymkhana somewhere in the Tendring District but the conversation quickly developed into a desire to revive the Tendring Hundred Farmers Club and its show after ten years of dormancy. It was a time when the mood amongst the farming community was as about as upbeat as anyone could remember. The Germans were in retreat on all flanks on the Continent to the point where victory now seemed a matter of when not if. On the home front the air raids that had peppered Tendring farms as the Luftwaffe emptied out anything that remained

Four men key to the post-war revival at the Tendring Show at the 1952 Show. From left to right - Show Director J. Fenn, Secretary P. Daniel, President A. Davidson, Chairman H. Hayward.

in their bomb holds on return from bombing London were long over. More generally, just as in the First World War, the importance of home farming when it came to feeding the nation was back in favour and an element of prosperity and vibrancy had returned to the local farming scene. Once more the plough had returned to the fields of the Tendring Hundred.

At a meeting at the Colchester Corn Exchange in the April of 1945 things came to a head when the newly elected committee debated whether they should hold a show in July. John Fenn had identified two possible sites for the Show just south of Great Bromley either side of Parsons Hill. The question was whether it was appropriate to hold a show while there was a war on. Opinion was deeply divided. Some felt the time was right to resort to

Colchester Corn Exchange. A key meeting place for the Club both in 1899 and 1945.

some normality and inject some fun into the social life of farmers after five long years of war and the misery that came with it. There was an infectious feeling that while there was momentum, particularly among some of the younger farmers, then the opportunity should be seized. On the other hand others had grave reservations about reviving the Show while the many local farming families still had sons away from home fighting in Europe or the Far East. There were also minor matters such as Petrol rationing to consider. Although it would be allowable to use coupons for the purpose of education it was debatable that the authorities would agree that all those at the Show were there just for that earnest purpose. After much debate caution won out over impulsiveness and things were put off for another year in the hope that by then the hostilities would be over.

Wix Young Farmers at the 1951 Show in the judging competition.

The great tide of 1953.

The Tug of War Committee at the revival show in 1946.

Fortunately the momentum was not lost and the revival show was held on 13th July 1946. Alongside the commanding John Fenn we should mention here Herbert Hayward and Victor Crisp who worked hard alongside Fenn in his determination to reinstate the Show back into the Tendring Hundred calendar. Hayward acted as Chairman for many years and Crisp agreed to be the first post-war President later becoming treasurer. The Haywards were a long standing Gt. Bromley family who farmed at Badley Hall Farm. Herbert was a keen breeder of pedigree Suffolk Sheep and Large White pigs which partly explains his enthusiasm for the revival of a show that provided opportunity for local farmers to show off their prize livestock. Crisp was a Director of Brooks of Mistley (see Chapter 5) who sold animal feed and seeds. Between them as agent, farmer and trade - Fenn, Hayward and Crisp represented

1946   Back Row: Dick Mitchell, Jock Pirie, John Lowe, Philip Giles, John Black.
Sitting in Front: Bob Halsall, Andrew Davidson, Andrew Mitchell.

a solid triumvirate on which to rebuild the Show. We should not forget here the hard working Secretary with a salary of £150 a year was the only paid official of the club. Despite the remuneration, in the 1940s and 1950s the club seemed to struggle to retain a Secretary for more than a couple of years.

After the war, now that the concept of the weekend was established, a Saturday was chosen rather than the previous tradition of holding the Show mid-week. From then on the Tendring Show was always held on the second Saturday in July just as it is today. The habit of moving the Show geographically every year was also abandoned but other than a rather rudimentary ex-army Nissan hut, which

Mr. J. Stone and his daughter Maureen with their mare and foal at the 1953 show. The mare had been rescued from the deluge of the great tide of 1953 which on the night of January 31st had consumed much of the Essex coast drowning hundreds of people and thousands of animals. The presence of the foal at the show was a silver lining on what had been a very black night for many Tendring farmers who woke the following morning to find their farms consumed by several feet of the North Sea. The foal won a commendable Second Prize.

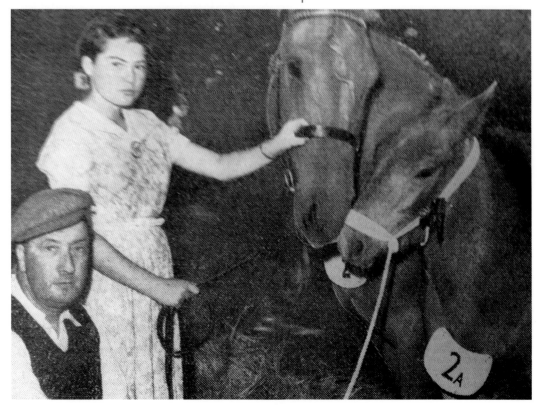

could be picked up very cheap once the war was over, no other showground 'fixtures' were established. In the immediate years after the war the Show was a rather basic affair. Many competitors in the horse jumping competition would ride their horses along roads to the Show in the morning and tie them up in surrounding hedges as they waited their turn.

The Showground was a field behind the Gt. Bromley cricket ground tenanted by the Girling family. It was deemed to have a pleasant sheltered aspect with good road access. But at twelve acres the site was on the small side. For the thirteen years that the Show stayed at Gt. Bromley, space always seemed at a premium. As showground Directors, John Fenn and his successor, Robert Harding, were always

Not a cesspit pit for the 'Gentlemen's Conveniences' but rather a demonstration of a mechanical digger at the 1955 Show. In the 1950s machines were taking the back ache out of many jobs on Essex farms that had been done by hand.

juggling trying to cram more and more into the limited space. Soon the Show was spilling over into the outfield of the neighbouring cricket ground along with parking permitted on the extensive rectory lawns. This issue was made worse by the fact that members were allowed to park on the Showground around the Grand Ring. As car ownership doubled in the UK every decade after the war, the traffic congestion and parking issues both inside and outside the ground got worse and needed more and more management, not to mention liaison with the local police. Soon the locals were complaining about the number of cars parked up on the roadside verges all the way down Parsons Hill.

A bruised backside and possibly some bruised pride for the Hunt-master as he enters the Grand Ring at the 1956 Show.

MISHAP FOR THE MASTER

The perils of the English Summer. Many of the Shows in the 1950s were plagued with rain but never enough to cancel the Show or activate the Pluvius insurance policy.

Yet another competitor for ground space that gave John Fenn an annual headache was the increasing presence of trade stands at the Show. In the decade after the Second World War farming was going under immense change and the Tendring Hundred was very much at the forefront of these developments. The change was fundamentally pushed on by new technical development coupled with improved prosperity which enabled farmers to afford to buy into new ideas and techniques. After decades of depression the post-war years proved good ones for Tendring farmers. The 1948 Agriculture Act had brought in a system where the Government guaranteed prices. This gave farmers the confidence to invest in their farms after many years of neglect. In the farmyards, the old traditional buildings of thatch and wood were being swept away to be replaced by more functional buildings of concrete and steel. Out in the fields horses were being replaced by tractors. In 1945 there were an estimated million horses on British farms, just two decades later they had more or less all gone. Fortunately for the Show, horses continued to be found on farms but mainly for recreation. The way crops were grown was also changing. Artificial fertilisers were replacing muck. Agrochemicals to control pests, weeds and diseases were being introduced. New, higher yielding varieties were being bred. In the livestock sector, new improved breeds were being introduced as was A.I. Farmers now increasingly bought in their animal feed in improved rations rather than growing it themselves. One fundamental way that this was changing the Tendring Show was it caused a proliferation of trade stands. Farmers were buying and selling far more than they used to. New machines, animal feeds, fuels, herbicides, buildings, new seeds - all found in shop windows at the agricultural show. Manufacturers, merchants and dealers were competing hard for the expanding farmers trade and in response a modest level of corporate entertainment was introduced. The custom for farmers at the Show was now to find a decent free lunch if not two or three. Trade stands got bigger to accommodate what were basically free restaurants for hungry farmers.

Although farming in the Tendring Hundred was changing quite rapidly in the post war era

Standing from front:
DENNIS GARNER   AGNES LOWE (Barrie)   BILL LEIPER

Photo - " East Anglian Daily Times "

ERICA LENNOX   SAM COOPER   PANDORA SARSON   DAVID GREENACRE   MICK GLOVER
JEAN SCHWIER   GORDON SCHWIER   MICHAEL WRIGHT   JIM EADY

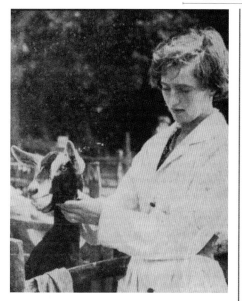

Below: Mr. P. Evitt and his horn - a regular sight and sound at the Shows in the 1950s and 1960s.

the demise of the mixed farm was still to come. Although the area was known for its ploughed acres rather than permanent grazing, most farms still kept sheep, cows or pigs along with heavy horses to pull the plough. Because of this the showing of livestock remained an integral part of the Show just as it had at its inception fifty years previous. By 1948 the Show had 68 cattle entries, 54 pigs, 92 sheep and 81 goats. As a sign of the changing times, in 1953 the Milk Marketing Board gave a prize for the best dairy cow produced through artificial insemination. Another demand on space at the initial 1940s shows was the fact that TT (Tuberclin Tested) cattle were required to be kept in their own separate ring isolated from non-tested cattle. The post-war era saw huge advances in animal

health on farms which meant more and more dairy herds were securing much prized TT status which meant they did not want to risk infection by mixing with those that weren't. In an era before TB vaccination in the human population, we should remember there were important human health issues here as well. By the 1950s the TT ring was scrapped as the show committee ruled that all cattle should be proven clean of TB. But other infectious diseases such as Foot and Mouth and Swine Fever still occasionally haunted the Show. The severe Foot and Mouth outbreak in 1952 was particularly devastating as it precluded all cloven hoofed animals from appearing at the Show.

It was in the forties and fifties that many Tendring farms were first connected to mains water and electricity which facilitated more technical development and improvement, not to mention extra domestic comfort. The Showground at Bromley received the benefit of running water for stock in 1950 but it was decided not to extend the pipe to that part of the ground which often proved the show committee's greatest challenge - namely the Ladies conveniences. While the Gentlemen could make do with a crudely screened long trough sloping towards a large hole in the ground (strictly a 'stand up job' only), the fairer sex needed more sophisticated arrangements for obvious reasons. Throughout the Bromley years the largely male show committee were constantly bombarded with complaints about the state of affairs in the Ladies with demands

Hijinks at the 1957 show - before Health and Safety was invented.

for improvements such as cubicles with doors. Despite an enquiry to the 'Mosan Mobile Powder Rooms Co' to provide a more purpose built structure on skids, it was considered too expensive. Meanwhile back in the farmhouses and the farm cottages the outside privies were becoming a thing of the past and night soil men with their malodorous carts were put out of a job. The gates at the Bromley Shows were never spectacular starting off with a commendable 5000 paying £500 in 1946 but never rising above 6500 and sometimes sinking to below 3000 in 1956 when bad weather struck. In the 1950s the Show developed a reputation for being unlucky with the weather with frequent rainy shows. In 1951 the committee chose to splash out on a Pluvius policy costing £25 giving £250 cover but as no show was actually cancelled due to wet weather it seems it was never actually called upon. Despite the occasional indifferent weather, the Eldorado Ice Cream Co. were always prepared to bid £10.00 for a stand to sell their ice creams.

More generally the Show seemed to avoid catastrophe. There was always the occasional riderless hose which having thrown its rider in the Grand Ring would canter around the Show ground scaring small children and nervous dogs. In 1957 the Presidents marquee caught fire from a discarded cigarette but seeing as it was late in the afternoon most show-goers never even got to know about the blaze until they read about it in the paper the following week.

Generally the Show gained a reputation for its 'intimate and friendly atmosphere'. It was said that farmers went to the County shows such as the Essex or the Suffolk to do business whereas at the Tendring Show they went primarily to meet each other. Writing in 1955 a visiting journalist described it as 'the perfect combination of the local and the familiar with something different every year'. In 1953 there was a special visitor to the Show in the form of Ibrahim Natoo, the Kenyan Minister of Works who commented 'It is delightful here, a wonderful setting, but do not let it get any bigger. It is just the right size.'

Unlike the pre-war years when THFC meetings were held in the winter to discuss agricultural issues, the post-war club at first

Three stalwarts of the Show in the 1950s and 1960s - John Macaulay, Arthur Webb and Atfield Brooks, taking a breather on their shooting sticks.

concentrated solely on putting on the Show. The War had seen the establishment of the Thorpe Discussion Group in 1942 which meant the Tendring Hundred now had its own dedicated organisation that brought the district's farmers together to learn about technical developments in agriculture. Meeting once a month through the winter at the W.I. Hall in Thorpe, the group was typical of many farmer groups established during the war with the aim of improving agriculture by putting different experts in front of farmers in a social setting where they could compare notes between each other. In 1943 over eighty Tendring Farmers met to hear a discussion entitled 'Can the Tractor entirely replace the horse on the modern farm?'. Although there was a huge overlap between THFC and Thorpe Discussion Group in terms of membership, the two organisations ran quite separately.

A timeless scene from the 1957 show.

Despite this concentration on just running the Show in the 1940s, the club decided to run an annual ploughing match in the autumn from 1950 to 1957. There had been a ploughing match in Bromley before the war so it wasn't long before someone suggested to the committee they should revive it. It was given to the young farmers to organise using club funds. At first the day was reasonably well attended with both horses and tractors taking part with the latter outnumbering the former two to one. The 'Tractor and Trailer Driving competition' that took up valuable space at the Show in the 40s was moved to the ploughing match. A root and produce show was also added in 1951. But after initial success the ploughing match and its associated competitions seemed to struggle to get many entries. Bad weather and late harvests were blamed as was the demise of the heavy horse. In 1957 the Show committee decided it could no longer justify the £150 expense of putting the day on and it was duly cancelled. By way of some mitigation the Club introduced a Tractor Parade in 1958 in the Grand Ring.

In 1958 the Club was a victim of the general improvement of grassland that was becoming the norm across the agricultural scene in that the Showground field itself was drained and reseeded by the tenants. In the post-war decades thousands of acres of UK farmland were drained to make it more productive usually with the assistance of Government grants. The problem for the Club was that this meant the ground would lack the necessary

Above: The young ladies of Wix Young Farmers take the strain at the 1957 show

...and a similar scene 50 years later

grass cover in July. The solution proved to be not very far away. The Club Chairman, Herbert Hayward's own farm was at Badley Hall just on the other side of Parsons Hill and he offered his grounds for the 1958 show. Tragically Herbert Hayward died just months before the Show and the Hayward family felt hosting the Show would have to be for just one year only. As before, the Showground field was to be ploughed and reseeded to improve the grass. Once again, the Tendring Show was in need of a new home but the short term challenge proved fortuitous for long term prospects in that it gave a much needed opportunity in 1959 to find a larger home that would better fit the expanding Show.

Chapter Five

THE BROOKS OF MISTLEY

The firm that was known as 'Brooks of Mistley' has an intrinsic involvement with both the history of the Tendring Show and the wider farming scene which is worth noting in this story, that spans three centuries.

The port of Mistley was established in the 1720s at the western end of the deeper water of the Stour estuary. The newly founded port

Aerial view of the Brooks complex at Mistley Quay in the 1950s with the 'Blister Hut' sack-store on the right behind the famous Mistley Towers then working right to left ware-houses, maltings, railway sidings and mill.

A special consignment of Red Clover seed grown in Tendring, bagged at Mistley and driven to London Dock for shipment to Canada.

was famously sketched in its early years by John Constable when fine-tuning his artistry in the Dedham Vale.

The port quickly became a focal point for the local agricultural economy. As such, it naturally attracted warehouses, maltings and mills. The business that became Brooks of Mistley can be traced back to eighteenth century maltings on the quay-side owned by the Norman family. In the 1860s the Norman family left the business to loyal employee William Brooks. In those days farming, merchanting and milling were all part of the business. In the decades around the turn of the twentieth century, under the direction of William's son and grandson, both also called William, the company expanded into seed growing gaining an international reputation exporting seeds across the world - most famously Red Clover and Linseed grown in the Tendring Hundred.

In the 1920s the Brooks family reduced the thousand acres of local farmland they owned to just two hundred which were used as an experimental station for their products. One of those key products was their famous GB Cow Cubes which they show-cased by feeding them to their own herd of prize winning Red-Poll cattle kept at Trinity Farm between Mistley and Lawford. The Red Poll herd regularly picked up first prizes at prestigious shows such as the National Dairy Event. Bulls from the herd were also exported across the globe. This tradition of the Company showcasing the farming of the Tendring Hundred across the

Above: W.H.H. Brooks (centre) with his prize winning Red Polls at the 1932 Show

The Red Poll herd at Trinity Farm between Mistley and Lawford.

world continued when it took locally grown seed samples to the Toronto World Winter Fair, where prizes were often won including first prize in 1957 for some wheat grown by the Davidson family of Wix.

As a family, the Brooks were keen supporters of the Show. They can be found, along with the Normans, at the events in Thorpe in the 1830s as well as at the inaugural show in 1899. The son of William Brooks III, Charles Norman Brooks, was Show President in 1911 when the Show was held on land owned by the family at Mistley. His cousin, William Hilton Brooks was President at the last pre-war show in 1933 also held at Mistley. Victor Crisp who was

Harvesting pure bred Wheat Seed at the Brooks experimental station in the 1950s.

Company Director was President at the revival show in 1946 and after that he was treasurer for many years. In the post-war revival years the Club invested much of its money with Brooks at a guaranteed rate of 3.5% with instant access to the fund if ever required. Continuing the family tradition, Charles Norman's son, Charles Atfield Brooks was President in 1960. After that Sir Philip Southwell and Charles Bolton who sat on the Brooks board were both Presidents and key supporters of the Show. We should also not forget here the likes of Bob Sarson, a well known and much liked salesman come-ambassador for the company in the Tendring area, who manfully stewarded

The Brooks stand at the 1958 Show. A snazzy frontage leading to the luncheon marquee.

Part of the Brooks stand at the 1958 Show.

the Grand Ring for many years. Furthermore the Brooks trade stand was a regular fixture at shows throughout its first seventy years of it's history. They also showed their Red Poll Cattle, often picking up cups and prizes. Brooks staff were always available to help out when needed in the running of the Show as were Brooks offices if a meeting venue was needed.

In the 1960s, as was often the case with the smaller family companies in British manufacturing and commerce, Brooks of Mistley was acquired by a much larger outfit - the national milling giant 'Joseph Rank Group' who themselves later merged into Rank Hovis MacDougal. Although the Brooks name carried on for a short while, the brand was soon absorbed into RHM. In the 1980s the agricultural division of RHM was acquired by the Dalgety Group which, in turn, morphed into Masstock ten years later.

Today, the once thriving malting-milling hub of commercial activity that characterised Mistley port is more or less gone. Mills and Maltings have been turned into luxury flats. But it is right to remember and record the firm of Brooks of Mistley which gave Tendring farmers an international reputation and did much to support the Tendring Show both at its inception and in its hours of need during its first seventy years of history.

Chapter Six

TO LAWFORD AND THE ESTABLISHMENT OF A
BIG LITTLE SHOW

As we move into the second half of our story its worth taking note of the changes that were fundamentally altering the Tendring Hundred and thereby affecting the Show. In the first half of the twentieth century, the population of the Tendring Hundred had quadrupled to over 100,000 and this figure would have been more than doubled in the

The Members Tent at the 1961 Show.

summer by what were affectionately known by the locals as 'bloomin' holiday-makers'. The main concentration of this burgeoning resident and tourist population was along the east coast where, in a sweep of twentieth century development from Jaywick, through Clacton, Frinton and Walton ending in Harwich, a population of 80,000 had found a sea-side home. Even, the inland villages were not immune from this influx of new residents with many of them such as St. Osyth, Weeley and Elmstead changing out of recognition as the Greater London Council pursued its policy of moving people out of over-crowded inner London into the newly built housing estates that now peppered north east Essex. The district's roads were also changing with

First Prize for Mr. Jiggens Sheep - having just returned from being shown at the Royal Show. While a few Tendring farmers such a John Jiggens continued the Tendring tradition of breeding prize winning Suffolk Sheep, generally by the 1960s it was a declining aspect of Essex farming.

far more traffic. Throughout the interwar years, rough farm tracks had increasingly been 'adopted' by the Highway authorities to become Tarmac roads where cars, lorries and motorbikes could speed along. No longer could farmers peacefully drive their stock along the high-ways and by-ways of the Tendring Hundred.

But while the Tendring Hundred became a far busier and more crowded place in the first half of the twentieth century, the number of farmers and farm workers halved to less than 2000 in number. Increasing mechanisation meant farms could be run with less farmers and less labour. As the machinery stands at the Show attested, tractors and combines were becoming bigger with greater technical complexity which meant a post-war farmer driving a machine could achieve work rates that a pre-war farmer

A state of the art 'aerial' tractor at the 1961 Show.

By the 1960s agriculture in the Tendring Hundred was rapidly changing and the Tendring show was changing with it.

with a heavy-horse could only have dreamt of. Farming was also becoming more specialised and the traditional mixed farming was starting to disappear. Herbicides and artificial fertilisers meant that it was possible to farm without grazing livestock in a field rotation. The Essex marshes that had for centuries been grazed by sheep and cows had been ploughed up during the war-time push for greater self sufficiency in food with its emphasis on producing calories through crops rather than meat. Even the black faced Suffolk Sheep that the Hundred had boasted prize winning flocks of were becoming rare. The milking cow was also becoming an endangered species. In the agricultural austerity of the interwar years many Tendring farms had turned to dairying as one of the few sectors that showed a profit. The Milk Marketing Board established in 1930 guaranteed prices while the London market gave a nearby outlet

Since the Second World War, farm machinery has got bigger and more sophisticated on the farms of the Tendring Hundred. At the 2000 Show Ernest Doe demonstrated this well in the Grand Ring.

with churns being delivered to train stations for collection. Before the Second World War every parish in the Tendring Hundred could boast several dairy farms, from larger herds of Friesians and Jerseys milked by machine to smaller farms with just a handful of shorthorns milked by hand. But in the 1950s and 60s many milking herds started to disappear. Foot and Mouth epidemics in the 1950s caused many to throw the towel in. By the 1990s the Tendring Hundred could boast only a handful of dairy herds. Similarly pig keeping, which for most Tendring farms in the interwar years was primarily a good way of disposing of scraps in a few traditional sties in the farmyard became far more specialist with a few dedicated units keeping stock indoors in efficient conditions. The 1960s saw the final swansong of the heavy horse. The tractor was now king.

In 1989 there was a line up from yesteryear as a reminder of a time when no self respecting farmer went without a little grey fergie.

This decline in livestock numbers and of livestock farms had an obvious impact on the Show. Before the 1960s the main 'raison d'être' of the Show was for farmers to show prize winning livestock. This had been the key driver for John Eagle, the father of the Show, in 1899. But after 1960 this emphasis was to change. While farm livestock remained an integral part of the Show it was becoming harder and harder for the Committee to pull in entries. Another hurdle was animal health regulations which frequently prevented animals being brought to the Show. Several shows in the late 60s and early 70s saw no cattle classes because of Brucellosis outbreaks. From the 1990s it became increasingly difficult to attract pigs to the Showground because of concerns about infectious diseases. In 2001 the worst happened when the Show had to

A Foot and Mouth Disease pyre in the 1950s. Infectious animal diseases often plagued the Tendring Show causing classes to be cancelled. FMD caused the 2001 Show to be cancelled.

be completely cancelled due to the national outbreak of Foot and Mouth disease. Although the highly infectious disease was first identified in Essex at an abattoir near Brentwood, it was never found on any Tendring Hundred farms. Nonetheless Tendring farmers took vigilant measures to make sure it never did infect their stock. When the Show executive met in the spring of 2001 they were aware that as FMD only affected cloven-hoofed animals it was still possible to hold the Show with horses and small animals in attendance but the problem was the virus could be spread by dirt on farm vehicles and, indeed, on the farmers themselves. It was felt that as thousands of cows and sheep were being slaughtered in western and northern Britain to contain the disease then it was only right that Tendring farmers should do their bit to minimise the chance of transmission. At great expense and at great sacrifice the 2001 show was duly cancelled thus ending a run of fifty-five continuous annual shows.

While showing local prize-stock may have declined in the Tendring Hundred, the enthusiasm for amateurs to show off 'smaller' animals has not.

At the 1979 show there was a daring attempt to launch a hot air balloon from the Grand Ring. As it struggled to gain height and as a sudden breeze picked up it looked at one point as if it might wipe out 99% of all known trade-stands. Mercifully a couple of big blasts on the burners gave it enough hot air to merely brush the tops of some of the perimeter oak trees as it made its graceful way in a north easterly direction. Last seen somewhere over Felixstowe.

Above: Raising the bar. The main driver for the original founders of the Show in 1899 was to create an annual event where Tendring Farmers could enter classes of competitions to breed better stock and improve their farming. Today the Club inherits that spirit of competition and improvement. It has a rich legacy in the form of a vast array of silverware to prove it.

Louise Smith receiving a silver salver for her Holstein cow in 2000 from Janet MacDonald.

Above: The Hutchbys - winners of the best stand at the 2010 Show with Chairman T. Isaac and President M. Carr.

Throughout the post-war era THFC has always maintained close links with Wix and Colchester Young Farmers Clubs. In the 1950s judging competitions were held for young farmers on the Show day. The young farmers also organised the club ploughing match. As these two photos show, one from the 1960s and one fifty years later, the young farmers also provided great entertainment in the Grand Ring with various races involving complex challenges. In the 1970s one competition involved a female young farmer being bound with rope and then manhandled over an obstacle course by male club members. Today one suspects such activity would not be considered politically correct - even if we are all reading 'Fifty Shades of Grey'.

In the 1950s the Tendring Show was known as 'The friendly show' where Tendring farmers met socially for a catch up. Fifty years later, as the photo from the 2007 show illustrates, this is still very true today.

Above: Hot show weather isn't just thirsty work for the show-goers, the exhibits need looking after as well.

These twin challenges of declining numbers of farm animals and increasing restrictions on animal movements meant that the number of locally reared cows, pigs and sheep was declining on show day. One compensation was that exhibitors were coming from further afield with some travelling hundreds of miles. But, almost perversely, the number of animals on the Showground did not necessarily diminish. While the commercial stock of cows, sheep and pigs declined the numbers of small animals exhibited by hobbyists increased. Goats, rabbits and fowl had been part of the Show since the 1920s but in the decades after the war the variety of animals shown by amateurs increased. Over time the

Show-goers queuing up to get into the 1996 Show. Since the 1950s the attendance at the Show has increased 500% from around four thousand to well over twenty thousand. This larger crowd combined with the fact the Tendring Hundred has become more urban since the war has meant audience for the Show has changed significantly. Although the Show has responded to this change it has kept agricultural and rural life at its heart. The Tendring Show is true to its roots but not stuck in its ways.

Show has seen an increasing variety of animals which has even included fancy rats. Quite what the early show-founders such as John Eagle would have thought of Rat classes we can only guess at. Even the current day Tendring farmers have been known to refuse to enter the fancy rat tent for fear they cannot contain their uncontrollable instinct to grab a stick and bludgeon to death someone's prized and well groomed pet.

More generally, a rapidly expanding urban population in the Tendring Hundred alongside a shrinking farming industry meant the complexion of the Show going public would inevitably change and the Show would change with it. From its earliest days through to the 1950s the Show attendance had been around

Above: 'What do you mean I've got to breathe into a bag?' 1994 Show President Gordon Schweir looks a little apprehensive when he came across the boys in blue doing their rounds. In actual fact, no doubt Gordon and Club Chairman were thanking them for their much appreciated presence.

'Its not a hamster, it's a rat' - Jim MacDonald, Show President in 2000 casts a doubtful eye over the exhibits in the fancy rat tent.

4000 most of whom would have come from farms. The first Show in 1959 at the larger Lawford ground attracted a crowd of 5053 charging half a crown (2/6) for adults and 6d for children. After two o'clock in the afternoon you could enter at half price. It was at this time some of the more frugally minded in the farming community would turn up. By 1970

In 1992 the Show took a continental twist when a number of foreign visiting troupes were invited to parade in the Grand Ring. No jokes about good carcass conformation necessary.

the attendance had more than doubled to 11,000. With a much bigger gate with a less distinct farming origin, it was notable in the 1960s that the trade stands altered to reflect this. Also the 1960s saw the advent of the consumer society where post war austerity was becoming a thing of the past as working people could increasingly afford new conveniences and entertainments. A good example of this new type of trade stand was Page Motors who could be found at the Shows in the 1960s selling Morris cars. Similarly, a journalist who visited the Show in 1967 could but fail to be impressed that on the Williams and Griffin stand you could watch the Ladies Wimbledon Final between Billie Jean King and Anne Jones on a colour TV. What's more, show-goers could buy the set at a special show price of £299. And while you were at it, Willie Gee's would also sell you the latest mock leather PVC three piece suite to watch it on.

The practice of acknowledging at the Show the long and diligent service of those who work on farms was started by the Club in 1926. Today that well respected tradition is rightly maintained.

Above: Club President Buster Cooper escorts Princess Alice after a tree planting ceremony in 1985 to commemorate the Club's 75th Show. Mercifully everyone seemed oblivious to the fact that due to some miscounting it was actually the 71st.

1997 President Bob Wright looks ready for a quick dip as the pond in the Countryside area starts to fill the evening before the Show.

Above: Parkers Nurseries of Frinton bring a floral riot to the 2002 Show. A good example of a local business with farming connections adding to the colour of the Show.

Thrills and spills in the Grand Ring in 1998.

Two very similar scenes from Tendring Shows sixty-five years apart.

The next step change in attendance figures occurred in the 1990s when the gate pushed up towards the 20,000 mark finally surpassing it in 2000 at the Millennium show. One factor behind this trend for larger gates might have been the improving weather. Right from its early days until the 1970s the Show had frequently been plagued with bad weather and had a reputation as a wet, soggy show. The 1974 show was particularly badly hit with a sodden wet day resulting in a disastrously small attendance of 3,500 - the worst turn out since the 1956 show which also suffered persistent rain throughout the day. But from the years of the mid 1970s onwards, which were remembered for their blistering hot, dry, summers, the Show seemed to have a change of luck with very few rainy shows. This crowd pleasing run of good weather persisted right through until 2012 when the thirty year run of dry show days ended with a mud bath.

Braving the horse lines when the going got a bit soft at the 1962 Show.

A visitor to the 1975 Show dons the best known sun protection for bald heads.

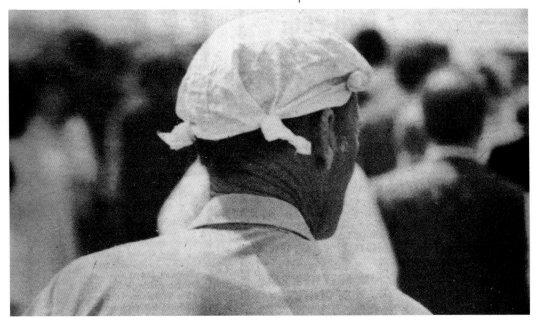

BUT SMILES DESPITE IT ALL

Above: The washed-out Show of 1974 that saw the attendance plummet by 4000. The good news was this would be the last thoroughly wet show until 2012.

And when you've stopped worrying about too much heat and too much rain at the Tendring Show, there's the little matter of too much wind.

Above: Chairman David Hunter (left) visits those men who often hold the fate of the Tendring Show in their hands at the 1995 Show with President Patrick Ireland.

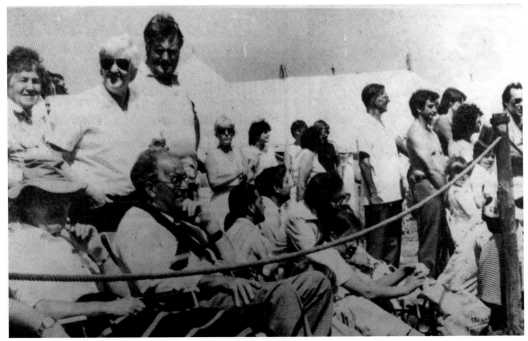

The hot dry summer of 1976 when the sun shone rather fiercely on ring-side spectators.

The Tendring Show is known for its sunny weather and happy show-goers.

As more black clouds loom, Club Vice Chairman Tim Isaac soldiers on at the 2012 Show.

🌿

Chapter Seven

A MAJOR ATTRACTION IN A FARMED FIELD

One of the charms of the Tendring Show is that it is held in a farmed field. In this respect it harks back to a centuries old tradition of holding fairs and shows in the working pastoral landscape of England.

For most the year The Tendring Show leaves little or no trace of its existence as Lawford Hall Park is returned to sheep grazing and a haylage crop.

Elsewhere, the vast majority of country and agricultural shows are nowadays held on dedicated show grounds with modern conveniences such as permanent buildings, concrete roads and sewers. But not in Tendring where, apart from one small barn and a few post holes, the Show leaves no trace of its existence. For eleven months of the year the field is farmed just as it was before the Show arrived there in 1959.

When, in 1958, the Show found itself in need of a new home it was the owners and tenants of Lawford House who came to its rescue. The house and grounds were owned by Mr. Rubeigh Minnie. Mr. Minnie had a colourful background in that he had found fame and fortune when he penned a book about 'Clive of India' in the 1930s. It went on to become

William Strang

a successful Hollywood film starring Ronald Coleman. With his resulting newly found wealth Mr. Minnie purchased Lawford House and the surrounding farmland as a home for his family. The farmland was tenanted by local farmer Mr. William Strang. Bill Strang was part of the recently arrived Scottish farming diaspora who travelled south to Essex in the 1920s. Having first followed the Fleming family to a farm near Chelmsford, Bill ended up at Stacies farm between Gt. Bromley and Lawford. Stacies farm had been part of the huge Rigby estate that extended all along the northern belt of the Tendring Hundred from Manningtree to Harwich in the eighteenth and nineteenth century. Like many of the great estates at the time, it fell apart in the early

The Show in the 1960s with the VP's cars parked round the Grand Ring cluttering up the ground and obscuring the view of the entertainment. Although it upset a few die-hards, the practice was abandoned without much complaint in the 1980s

Above: The final cut the fortnight before Show day.

Putting up the marquees.

twentieth century partly due to the new taxes on death duties but also due to the profligate ways of the incumbents. So by the 1930s many of the old Rigby Estate farms were an available opportunity for a number of newly arrived Scottish emigrant families to make a new home. At Stacies William also tenanted the twenty eight acre field at Lawford House that was to become the home of the Show from 1959 onwards. When Bill Strang died in the early 1960s the tenancy was taken on by one of William's four daughters Liz, who had married local farmer Lindsay Lennox. It was about this time that Rubeigh Minney sold the house and land but before he did he wrote into the tenancy agreement that the tenant would have a right to hold the Show in the grounds.

Above: Pegging out the week before. A task that's probably as old as the Show itself but possibly made a little more accurate with CAD plans.

Chairman Will Powell, President Margery Wright, Show Director Robert Harding and Secretary Mr. Dixie pore over plans for the 1966 Show at the Showground.

Above: Girl power and flower power. Mandy Rix (left) the Tendring Hundred Farmers Club's first and only lady Chairperson.

This proved a very valuable clause when subsequent owners of Lawford House unveiled development plans for the park land that would have prevented the Show from taking place.. The plans had to be shelved as Club lawyers pointed out that thanks to Rubeigh Minnie's benevolence and the Lennox's goodwill the Show was protected in that the tenant had a right to allow the Show to be held on the site for at least one day a year.

Because of this insecurity over their rights to their showground home, the club has occasionally looked into finding an alternative ground for the Show but the Lawford site has always remained the preferred location. Fortunately for the Show the Lennox family remained firm supporters of it. Without this support the Show may well have had to follow the itinerant habits it had before the war. This would undoubtedly have prevented the Show

from establishing itself as successfully as it has. Again it is evidence of how the Show has been built on the goodwill of the local farming community and local landowners.

In the 1970s as the Show grew and expanded beyond the confines of the 28 acre field, licence arrangements were come to with adjoining landowners such as the Marshalls, Tabor Farms and Pooles to provide additional car parking. In some years there was a rush to harvest early potatoes or barley so that fields could become car parks by the second week in July. This increasing demand for car park space was resolved to a certain extent in the early 90's when forty-nine acres of land to the immediate south of the Showground were purchased by

Above: Club Chairman John Lochore and Show Director David Brooks planting trees in 1992 on recently acquired land due south of the Show ground. Given that land prices have more than quadrupled since then it has proved a very prudent investment of Club funds.

Below: Chairman Bill Powell, far right, makes sure there aren't too many hurdles to overcome at the 1963 Show.

Above: Crossed legs queuing for the loos at the 1997 Show. The arrangements made for the Gentlemens and Ladies conveniences have often occupied the Show committee over the years. From rather primitive arrangements involving troughs leading to holes in the ground to the porta-loos that started to appear in the 1980s. Today the Show spends an eye-watering £10,000 so show-goers can spend a penny in comfort.

Below: Lawford House with the Show behind it in the 1980s.

the Club. At the time, the price of £1800 an acre was thought to be rather expensive by some farmers on the club executive committee but the purchase was persevered with as it was viewed as necessary for the good of the Show. In retrospect, given agricultural land prices are five to six times that today, it has proven an extremely shrewd place for the club to invest its money.

The demand for space on the Showground was greatly alleviated by the radical decision in the mid 1980s to no longer allow Vice Presidents to park cars around the grand ring. Aside from the issue of making extra space, this move not only opened the ringside view to the general public it also made things safer as aged drivers no longer weaved amongst the pedestrians. Naturally there were a few who complained about the demise of this ancient right of the VPs to avail themselves of an in-cab ringside view - a practice that went back to

the Edwardian shows - but most just wondered why it hadn't been done before.

Holding a major event in a farmed field may have a touching sense of charm and tradition but it is not without its challenges. In the 1960s the Showground felt a little too much like a grazed field with it being rough underfoot complete with the odd cow-pat. Today the ground is much more show-user friendly thanks to sympathetic farm management by the Lennox family. Through the autumn and winter sheep are grazed, then in the spring a crop of haylage is cut. This leaves a reasonably level and tight sward for when the show-build team move in during late June. The construction of the tented village in July is one

An aerial view of the Show in 2006. The tented village - that quintessential sight from an English summer. While many of the marquees may have switched from canvass to plastic, the atmosphere created remains timeless.

of those quintessentially English countryside scenes. The huge, voluminous white marquees rise from the ground to sit gracefully amidst the parkland trees like landlocked ice bergs floating in a verdant sea of Green. On show day as you approach the Showground from the Bromley Road the tops of the tents can be seen from a country-mile away like the snow capped peaks of a mini-mountain range. It is a sight that is as old as the Tendring Show itself.

The person behind the ground plan that turns a farmed field into the tented village is the Show Director. In this respect the Club has been lucky to attract three long serving men who have between them filled the post for the entire seventy years between 1945 and 2015. What is more they were all, in turn, colleagues at one firm - the Land Agents, Fenn-Wright of Colchester. It is a good example of how the Show has benefited from strong personal relationships. In 1945 the redoubtable John Fenn took command as Show Director to duly hand over to Robert Harding in 1953. At the time Harding was Fenn's newly recruited junior at the Fenn-Wright partnership and was told by Fenn he should become Show Director to 'get to know the locals'. Over the next thirty years Robert Harding dedicated considerable time and devotion to the Show. Some feel without him the Show might not have survived some tricky times in the 1970s when poor weather and poor attendances hit club funds. It is quite right that the Show still remembers Robert Harding by virtue of the fact the new small barn put up in 2007 is

The fast-wheeling Mr. Robert Harding, long-standing Show Director and great servant of the Show, at Lawford Hall Park in the early sixties.

known as 'The Harding Hut'. In 1990 Robert Harding handed over to David Brooks who has continued in the role. It was in Brooks time that technology transformed the job of planning out what went where and how. No longer is the Show Director and his assistant reliant on tape measures, mallets, pegs and strings. Now they have the benefit of digitised technology with its lasers and GPS mapping satellites that can identify a position on the ground to the nearest centimetre. But no doubt all this space age technology can be undone by the ancient art of moving a neighbouring stand holders fence a couple of feet on the evening before the Show.

Chairman Bill Powell and Secretary Mr. Dixie discuss traffic arrangements with the long arm of the law at the 1963 Show.

And while we make mention of the Show Director we must also acknowledge the most important cog in the Show machine - the Club Secretary. Just as with its Show Directors, the club has been lucky to benefit from long serving Secretaries which gave it organisational continuity. Before the war the post was held by one man, Ernest Wenden for over thirty years. During the 1940s and 50s the post changed hands quite rapidly but when the Show moved to Lawford in 1959 it secured the services of Mr. Dixie who in turn handed the job onto his wife, Mrs. Dixie, who in the 1980s duly handed it to her daughter Anne Taylor who kept the job on until the year 2000. This forty year secretaryship by one family gave the club a valuable inter-connectedness. It was in the FMD hiatus year that Anne Taylor handed over to Romany Foster who, at the time of writing, continues to fulfil the role with her well regarded efficiency and charm.

The show building gang taking a well earned rest in the old Nissan hut.

Above: Romany Foster takes the reins as Club Secretary from Anne Taylor in 2001. Between them, Anne and her mother and father - Mr. and Mrs. Dixie - had undertaken the Secretary role for over forty years.

Behind every good show there is a good looking committee.
Andrew Young, Show President in 2011, takes centre stage

Setting up the Art Show and at the 'preview' always held the evening before the Show. In the 1960s the Art Show was introduced as another aspect of he show. It has always proved a popular attraction both for budding local artists and for the art loving show-goer.

● The public address caravan at the Tendring Show really ought to be called Pandora's Box. For the woman who has been behind the microphone for 30 years is Mrs Pandora Sarson, of Gutteridge Hall Lane, Weeley.

If there was ever a 'voice' to be associated with the Tendring Show it has to be that of Pandora Sarson. Weeley resident Pandora provided Grand Ring commentary at the Show over forty years. Not only did she have to commentate on whatever was going on in the ring, she also had to announce the names of lost children over the tannoy. For those of a certain age the line 'Will Mr. and Mrs. Farnsbarns please come to the Secretary's tent where a rather distraught little Freddie is waiting rather impatiently for them' will be something they will always remember. Pandora's pitch perfect voice and crisp RP elocution made her the perfect choice to become the voice of the Tendring Show.

Pandora receiving a token of the Clubs gratitude in 1992 from Show President Andrew Smith.

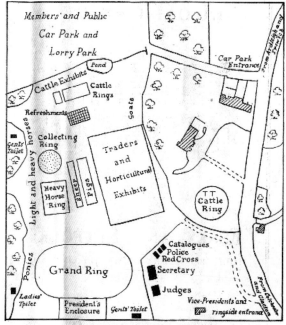

PLAN OF SHOWGROUND
Great Bromley, 1951

These two maps of the Showground in 1950 and in 2015 illustrate well how the Tendring Show has grown over the years.

Chapter Eight

FAST-TRACK FLOUR - FROM FIELD TO FORK

In 1988 the Show included an exhibition called ' The Wheat Story' as a way to explain to showgoers how the roadside fields of wheat turned into fresh loaves of daily bread. St. Osyth Wheat farmer, Roger Lord, was involved in its organisation. The sight of wheat mills and bread ovens at work on the Showground gave him an idea. If you could mill wheat and bake bread at the Show then you could probably do the same in a wheat field at harvest time? Hence the next question to occur was 'could the Club try to establish the minimum time needed for turning a standing wheat crop into a loaf of bread ready to eat?' Discussing the idea further with Club stalwarts - Messrs Macaulay, Lochore and Glover - a cunning plan was hatched.

On August 16th 1989 an array of harvesting and baking machinery and expertise was duly assembled at Wix in a wheat field farmed by Alan Davidson. A John Deere combine leant by machinery dealer Tuckwells started the race against time. The moment that threshed wheat appeared from the combine sieves it was raced

Tendring's answer to Usain Bolt, John Lochore, sprints to the mill with the world's freshest harvested wheat.

to a mill to be speed-ground into flour that was rapidly kneaded into dough to be slammed into a pre heated oven set for 'fast-bake'. As the dust settled and a recognisable loaf emerged, the stop-watch clocked a commendable 30 minutes 45 seconds. Those keepers of World Records - The Guinness Book of Records - confirmed that this was indeed the fastest time on earth that mankind had turned a wheat crop into bread. The trouble was that just a week later some dastardly American farmers in far-away

Team Tendring proudly display the worlds speediest Baker's Dozen.

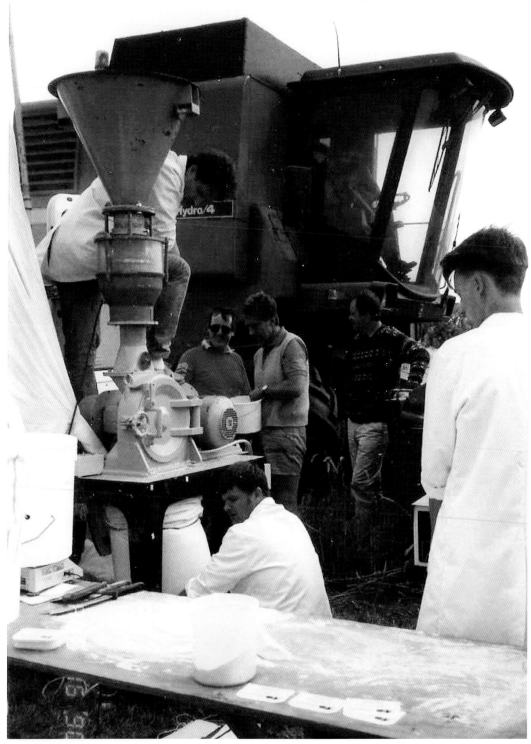

Messrs Lord and Macaulay oversee the milling undertaken by Norfolk millers Reed-Woodrow.

Texas heard of this Tendring Triumph and duly completed the exercise in under 30 minutes. Determined that this record should not leave Tendring's shores for long, our now even fitter THFC squad reassembled on August 23rd in a field owned by Jeremy Lyons at Ardleigh. Deploying the strategy of 'minimal gains' later made famous by the British Olympic Cycling team, the Tendring team shaved a whole four minutes off their previous efforts and re-seized the World Record at 26 minutes, 37 seconds.

But that was not the end of the story. Having got a taste for this extreme level of fast execution the team again reconvened at Roger Lord's Farm in St. Osyth to have one more grind. This time Team Tendring were clearly at the peak of corn condition and smashed their previous time turning in a breathless blur of 23 minutes 49 seconds.

As a rather mournful post-script to this little bit of local herculean history we ought to add that today this record is held by some dodgy Australians in New South Wales who claim a eye-popping time of 16 minutes 30.83 seconds (note we're now counting in hundredths of seconds). Doubts have been expressed about the quality of these Aussie loaves but maybe, because of less gravity, bread rises quicker down-under.

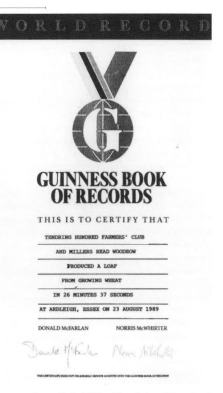

WORLD RECORD

GUINNESS BOOK OF RECORDS

THIS IS TO CERTIFY THAT

TENDRING HUNDRED FARMERS' CLUB

AND MILLERS READ WOODROW

PRODUCED A LOAF

FROM GROWING WHEAT

IN 26 MINUTES 37 SECONDS

AT ARDLEIGH, ESSEX ON 23 AUGUST 1989

DONALD McFARLAN   NORRIS McWHIRTER

THIS CERTIFICATE DOES NOT NECESSARILY DENOTE AN ENTRY INTO THE GUINNESS BOOK OF RECORDS

Its official! The Tendring Hundred Farmers Club make a little bit of agricultural history.

Above: Forty years early wheat was being harvested at Alan Davidsons farm in Wix at a rather more sedate pace. Its a reminder of how farming in the Tendring Hundred has changed over the years. The 1950s marked a time when machinery was taking over from horsepower.

A state of the art combine working in a field at St. Osyth Wick in 2013. It was part of a BBC programme about harvest which tried to calculate how many men with scythes and threshing sticks would be needed to achieve the work rate of a modern combine harvester. It was reckoned to be somewhere between five hundred and a thousand.

Chapter Nine

GETTING THE MESSAGE ACROSS

When the founders of The Tendring Hundred Farmers Club formed the organisation in 1899 they decreed in Rule 1 that the object of Club was 'to promote the cause of agriculture; to discuss subjects connected there with; and for such other purposes connected with Agriculture as may suggest themselves'.

The food tent in the late 1980s. At the time the Show was becoming a good opportunity to remind the consumers how their food is locally produced to the highest standards.

It was in the 1980s when agriculture increasingly came under a critical spotlight that the objective to 'promote the cause of agriculture' started to resonate strongly with many in the Club. There was a new appetite to use the Show and the Club as a means to get key messages over about farming to the non-farming public. It should also be remembered that the Club is a charity whereby it has an obligation to inform and educate.

Of course, by showing well groomed beasts and exhibiting the latest farm machinery the Show always fulfilled some of that role. But as the post war years of rationing merged into the time of EU grain and butter mountains many

The kitchen in the Food Tent in the 1990s. As the celebrity chef became a popular fixture on our TVs in the 1990s, the Show reproduced its own local real-life version to remind people that food and farming were intrinsically related. The connection between the two maybe obvious to the farming community but it is easily overlooked by the rest of the food chain. By bringing the kitchen to the Show it places it in the heart of the industry that provides the raw ingredients.

in the agricultural community thought that farmers were in danger of getting an unfair and negative image. This was also the time of various food scares such as the Salmonella crisis provoked by the ill-considered words of Government Minister Edwina Curry that caused the sale of eggs to halve overnight. Furthermore the media never seemed short of an alarmist story about the dangers of 'Factory Farming'. While agriculture struggled to defend itself in the face of ever noisier and well resourced detractors, many realised the Show was an under-used opportunity to showcase agriculture and to reassure consumers that British farm produce was produced to world beating animal welfare and food-safety standards as well as reminding show goers that farmers looked after the countryside keeping it in good heart.

An early attempt to promote British food at a show in the 1970s.

It was, in part, this incentive that lead to three new sections of the Show to be introduced in the 1980s - the Schools Tent, the Countryside Area, the Food Tent and the Theme area.

From 1990 to 2000 the Club also ran a Schools Open day where local Sixth Firm students were invited to a local farm to hear about agriculture from local farmers.

Above: President Lindsay Lennox in 1987 with wife Liz and Chairman Jim Macauley with the winners of the programme cover competition. The competition is open to all Tendring Primary Schools. Over the years it has got thousands of entries. The Tendring Hundred Farmers Club have always tried to pro-actively engage with young people about both the Show and about local agriculture. Children are the show-goers and consumers of tomorrow so farmers and the Show would do well to invest in them today. The programme cover competition is an ingenious way to do just that. By getting a wide and enthused response it promotes the Show and farming to a young audience - not forgetting their Mums and Dads.

The Schools Tent - a popular attraction that engages a crucial part of the Tendring Community.

Above: The Countryside Area - a chance to introduce young people to the delights of the Countryside and Countryside sports.

Gunning for a punt at the 2003 Show.

Above: The idea behind the Schools Day was to take groups of ten students round a series of stops on a working farm. Each stop covered a different aspect of agriculture. Here the men from British Sugar explain the intricacies of growing sugar beet and, thereby, where sugar originally comes from. From field to fork.

Above: Peter Giles oils the larynx while Bob Clarke gives the patter about potatoes.

Roger Lord and George Wright discuss the poor returns from farming from the back of a Series 3 Range Rover.

Each year at the Schools open day, in addition to students, VIPs were also invited. These were a selection of 'movers and shakers' drawn from Government, Media and NGOs. The idea was to get opinion formers and decision makers onto a farm so they could better understand the challenges of running a farm business first hand. It was not unknown for a leading civil servant from the Ministry of Agriculture to depart with the comment ' that was a really fascinating day - made all the more interesting by the fact I've never been on a farm before.' Here a group of VIPs huddle in at a rather drizzly open day in 1996.

Above: Every year a section of the Showground is designated the theme area where something eye catching is created with a message about agriculture behind it. In 2010 a 'straw henge ' was built to explain the importance of the seasons in farming. The henge was designed so that as the sun rose on show day the first shadow cast by the heel bale struck the master bales of the straw-sarsen. And if you believe that, you'll believe anything.

In 2004 the theme was called 'Construction of the Countryside'. The point being made was that the 'furniture of the countryside' - that being things like ditches, ponds, hedges and dry stone walls were not natural but rather were put there by farmers and maintained by farmers.

Above: The 'Home and Gardens' tent in the 1980s where judges deliberate over the respective merits of rival courgettes - having spent hours choosing the champion potato.

1989 President Robert Harding is given a working demonstration that explains to the public that milk doesn't actually come from Tescos.

Above: The theme in 1990 was 'Town and Country'.

In 1994 the theme was speed.

Above: In 2002 the theme area exhibited 'Pizza Farm'. A giant Pizza was cooked on a giant heated turn-table by Mark David in the middle of a Hexagonal farm which incorporated ingredients for the Pizza. Wheat for flour for the base, Cows for the cheese, greenhouses to grow tomatoes, pigs for the salami, Oilseed Rape for the cooking oil and herbs for the garnish. The claim was it was the largest Pizza on earth (at that moment in time).

In 2005 the Pizza farm concept was adapted to exhibit 'Pavlova Farm'. (The strawberries and Cream were real but the meringue was courtesy of B&Q quality insulation material).

Above: In keeping with the Show's ambition to educate as well as entertain, in the Grand Ring every year there is a half hour slot both in the morning and afternoon which seeks to give the Show-going public a better understanding of an aspect of agriculture. In 2011 the crowd were asked to imagine that the Grand Ring was a field growing wheat. Sequentially the story was told through a parade of cultivators, drill, sprayer and finally the combine harvester.

And in 2014 the growing and harvesting of sugar beet was the topic.

Postscript

As I write these notes, the preparation is well underway for the 100th Show. The haylage has been cut by the Lennox family and removed from the Showground - not forgetting the surrounding fields which will be used as car parks. The tents and stands have been mapped out by CAD and Show Director David Brooks knows exactly what will go where on show day. Show Secretary Romany Foster has taken all the stand bookings and reports that pre-show tickets are selling well on the web-site and entries for the Classes are up.

It is tempting to second-guess events by reporting that the 100th Show was a great success. To assume that the sun shone like it always does and that there was a bumper crowd in excess of 25,000 for the Centenary Show. We can probably take for granted that the President Jim Macaulay had a truly memorable day (even if he had seen over fifty shows before this one). We could predict that Club Chairman David Lord had an exhausting but rewarding day and his hundred strong team of bowler hatted stewards undertook their voluntary roles with a professional alacrity. Finally we should be able to rest assured that the Show day passed without incident or accident with the only crisis being a couple of lost children who were quickly re-united with Mum and Dad. It is tempting to assume all this will be the case because this is the usual form but we can't be 100% sure. It might rain all day like it has on rare occasions in the past with tractors pulling cars out of thick mud in the car park. Foot and Mouth disease might suddenly break out in Essex causing the Show to be cancelled. There may be a serious incident where a rider-less horse ends up in the Members Tent sending scones and sandwiches into the air. These things have happened before but they are the exception not the norm and a bookie wouldn't give you attractive odds on them happening in 2015.

Cover Design: '100 Shows - Then & Now' by Molly Nichols, Aged 8, Lawford C of E Primary School

Saturday 11th July 2015
PROGRAMME £3.00

Club Chairman David Lord captured by that most current form of photography - 'the selfie' taken from his Twitter account - at his farm at Earls Hall, St. Osyth. Note the blade of one of the five wind turbines on his farm. Also note the other person in the picture, his daughter Isabella - hopefully a future Chairperson for the Tendring Hundred Farmers Club, probably some time in the 2050s. David Lord is a highly suitable Chairman for the Centenary Show in that the Lord family are a long-standing Tendring Hundred farming family and they can be found throughout the history of the Show. Some of the early Shows at Thorpe were held on land farmed by the Lord family

What we can be sure of is that, on the day, toasts will be raised to the future of the Tendring Show. Club stalwarts will talk of how the Tendring Hundred Farmers Club must not rest on its centenary laurels but rather look to taking the Show forward as it now counts towards the 200th show. There might be some who will warn against complacency. Some might mention with some forboding the fact that the Essex Show and the Royal Show, both of which have out-rivalled the Tendring Show in the past, have recently collapsed and died.

There is no significant cause for alarm about the future of the Tendring Show. Its finances are in robust good order but not excessive. The Club holds a prudent level of reserves and assets to protect against a very rainy day. Its membership is healthy and historically high. The Show continues to pull in sizeable crowds that fit the Showground without swamping it or snarling up the local roads. The Club continues to successfully recruit the voluntary help it needs from the local agricultural and rural community. A younger generation is coming through to take on the task of running the show. Just as in the past the incumbent generation has recognised the responsibility that comes with inheriting the Show from those who came before, so to now it is important to hand that sense of responsibility on. The small, loyal, hard-working army of those who give up their time to put together the Show recognise its importance both in terms of what it does for the 'esprit de core' in the local farming and rural community as well as in how it is a valuable opportunity to reach out to the non-farming, urban, public. Farming needs its opportunities to promote itself to its consumers and the Tendring Show provides the industry with an excellent shop-window. It would be very unwise to lose that shop-window.

Just as the Tendring Hundred has changed immensely since Victorian times so too has the complexion of the crowd that turns up on Show day. The Show has responded to this change in audience by adding elements such as the Community area and the Education Tent. Over the years the Show has undoubtedly become less agriculturally 'hard-core' and opened itself up to celebrate all aspects of rural life - from keeping fancy rats to fly fishing. It also sells ground space to a much more varied amount of commercial interests. In 1899 businesses such as the Colchester Ironmongers Joslins, with their hay-carts and binders for sale were the only element of retail on the Showground other than the refreshment tents. Today the Showgoer is tempted by a huge range of different wares most of which have nothing to do with farming. But although the Tendring Hundred Farmers Club has not got stuck in its ways in what it is prepared to allow at its show, it is acutely conscious of its heritage. Its charm and its key selling points come from its strict agricultural origins. Without its farm animals or its farm machinery or indeed its farmers the Club would lose its soul. So policies are put in place to make sure this doesn't happen. Agricultural stand holders are given precedence over the double gazing salesmen. Farm stock competitions are cherished and maintained.

So as the Club and the Show look forward, it is reassuring to know it is in good heart. It is tempting to speculate how things will change in the future. When it started in 1899 the crowd arrived by horse or on foot with their shillings in their hands to gain entry. Today we book our tickets 'on-line' and arrive by the latest in motorised transport. When it comes to taking a picture as a momento of the Show, gone are the tripod cameras of 1900 afforded only by the rich - today we all take 'selfies' on our mobile i-phones and 'tweet' them to the outside world'. No doubt at the 200th Show in 2115 the average show-goer will arrive by a means of transport unimaginable today and have at their disposal technology embedded in some part of their anatomy we can currently only dream of.

If the Edwardian show-goer could somehow be transported to the 2015 Show they would no doubt be 'boggle-eyed' at what was on display. They would scratch their heads in disbelief at the huge tractors that have the necessary computerised satellite technology to drive themselves up and down fields without a human in control. They would stare in wonder at the airbourne drones that farmers use today to check stock and monitor crop development. They would struggle to understand that although dairy cows were still milked by hand, now it was by the hand of a robot not that of a dairy maid. But there would also be some aspects of the Show that the Edwardian time-traveller would be familiar with. The large white marquees. The prize stock being groomed to their best advantage. The rosettes that indicate the ' best in class'. The beer tent where some still get a little 'over-refreshed'. Above all its nice to think the 1899 Show-goer would also recognise the 'bonhomie' of the crowd having a fun day out. There is a key sense of continuity that threads through the first one hundred Tendring Shows but there is also a dynamic of immense change. The Tendring Show has stayed true to its roots while not getting stuck in its ways.

Guy Smith 15/06/15

A very modern way to advertise the 100th Show - taken by drone over Earls Hall Farm, St. Osyth.

The Tendring Hundred Farmers Club was formed at a meeting held on 22nd October 1898 at Colchester Corn Exchange where it was agreed to hold an annual show. The first thirty-one shows were held at various venues across the Tendring Hundred with a local farmer or dignitary chosen as President.

Date	Venue	President
1. 13/07/99	Thorpe Hall	J. P. Davis
2. 25/07/00	Mistley Place	C. K. Norman
3. 18/07/01	Comarques, Thorpe-Le-Soken	J. F. Round
4. 17/07/02	Bovills Hall, Ardleigh	W. Nocton
5. 15/07/O3	Wash Farm, Clacton	T. Lilley
6. 21/07/04	Ballast Quay, Elmsted	J. B. Hawkins
7. 20/07/05	Thorpe Hall	Lord Onslow
8. 19/07/06	Lawford Hall	P. Crossman
9. 18 /07/07	Hillside Farm, Weeley	J. P. Davis
10. 16/07/08	Convalescent Home, Clacton	T. Lilley
11. 15/07/09	Ardleigh Hall	W. Nocton
12. 21/07/10	Thorpe Hall	Ald. Wilson Marriage
13. 20/07/11	Park Meadow Mistley	C. N. Brooks
14. 18/07/12	Thorpe Hall	J. W. Eagle
15. 17/07/13	Wivenhoe Hall	H. K. Newton
16. 16/07/14	St. Osyth Priory	Lady Cowley
17. 16/07/19	Thorpe Hall	Sir Julian Byng
18. 14/07/20	Whitehall Farm, Weeley	P. Crossman
19. 20/07/21	Tower Meadow, Clacton	E. Gilders
20. 19/07/22	Thorpe Hall	M. Baker
21. 18/07/23	St. Osyth Priory	Brigadier General Kincaid-Smith
22. 16/07/24	Whitehall Farm, Weeley	H. Grimwade
23. 15/07/25	Park Lodge Meadow, Mistley	P. Crossman
24. 21/07/26	Michaelstowe Hall, Ramsey	R. C. Adby
25. 20/07/27	Thorpe Hall	Viscount Byng
26. 18/07/28	Gt. Bromley Hall	P. Crossman
27. 17/07/29	St. Osyth Priory	Brigadier General Kincaid-Smith
28. 16/07/30	Comarques, Thorpe	Lord Fairfax
29. 15/07/31	Michaelstowe Hall, Ramsey	R. C. Abdy
30. 09/06/32	Middlewick Ranges, Colchester	Rev. C. H. Brocklebank
31. 12/07/33	Park Lodge Meadow, Mistley	W. H. H. Brooks

After 1933 the Club fell dormant when British agriculture fell into severe depression but was revived in 1946. From then on a show was held every year on the second Saturday in July with the exception of 2001 when it was cancelled due to the Foot and Mouth epidemic. From 1946 to 1958 the Show was held in Great Bromley. From 1959 onwards it was held at Lawford House.

Date	President	Chairman
32. 1946	J. V. Crisp	H. Hayward
33. 1947	C. M. D. Gooch	L. T. Hinnel
34. 1948	C. A. Brooks	L. T. Hinnel
35. 1949	G. Cooper	L. T. Hinnel
36. 1950	G. E. Muers	L. T. Hinnel
37. 1951	Lt. Colonel Guy Blewitt	H. Hayward
38. 1952	A. Davidson	H. Hayward
39. 1953	G. Stanley Webb	H. Hayward
40. 1954	H. C. Hayward.	A. Davidson
41. 1955	Sir Philip Nichols	H. Hayward
42. 1956	John Macauley	H. Hayward
43. 1957	L. T. Hinnell	H. Hayward
44. 1958	J. Jiggens	A. H. Webb
45. 1959	M. R. Cobbold	A. H. Webb
46. 1960	C. A. Brooks	A. H. Webb
47. 1961	C. P. Harvey	A. H. Webb
48. 1962	Sir Philip Southwell	A. H. Webb
49. 1963	H. T. Hunneyball	W. C. Powell
50. 1964	K. J. Ireland	W. C. Powell
51. 1965	R. E. Giles	W. C. Powell
52. 1966	Mrs. M. C. Wright	W. C. Powell
53. 1967	J. R. Girling	W. C. Powell
54. 1968	V. A. Grantham	W. C. Powell
55. 1969	E. H. Cooper	H. H. Hunneyball
56. 1970	W. M. Impey	H. H. Hunneyball
57. 1971	H. Gibbon	E. B. Cooper
58. 1972	Dr. W. C. G. Baldwin	E. B. Cooper
59. 1973	R. Creswell	E. B. Cooper
60. 1974	P. W. Daniell	E. B. Cooper
61. 1975	W. C. Powell	A. H. Young
62. 1976	A. Faulds	A. H. Young

63.	1977	S. G. Grant	A. H. Young
64.	1978	J. N. Blyth	J. Macdonald
65.	1979	H. Gray	J. Macdonald
66.	1980	J. W. Eagle.	J. Macdonald
67.	1981	G. C. Gunary	A. R. Smith
68.	1982	O. A. Dunt	A. R. Smith
69.	1983	G. A. Woodburn	A. R. Smith
70.	1984	J. M. Pearce	A. R. Smith
71.	1985	E. B. Cooper	A. R. Smith
72.	1986	M. Lawrence	J. C. Macaulay
73.	1987	G. L. Lennox	J. C. Macaulay
74.	1988	J. C. Bolton	J. C. Macaulay
75.	1989	R. L. Harding	J. C. Macaulay
76.	1990	A. H. Young	J. C. Macaulay
77.	1991	G. Lockhart	J. C. Macaulay
78.	1992	A. R. Smith	J. Lochore
79.	1993	B. Chatto	J. Lochore
80.	1994	G. F. Schwier	J. Lochore
81.	1995	P. J. Ireland	T. Glover
82.	1996	H. F. Fairley	T. Glover
83.	1997	C. R. Wright	T. Glover
84.	1998	A. Davidson	T. Glover
85.	1999	J. Rayner	D. Hunter
86.	2000	J. Macdonald	D. Hunter
87.	2002	R. Steward	D. Hunter
88.	2003	P. Rix	R. Hutley
89.	2004	W. C. Rose	R. Hutley
90.	2005	P. A. Evans	M. M. Rix
91.	2006	P. Tuckwell	M. M. Rix
92.	2007	P. Fairs	M. M. Rix
93.	2008	G. Ellis	T. Isaac
94.	2009	H. Cobbald	T. Isaac
95.	2010	M. Carr	T. Isaac
96.	2011	A. Young	T. Isaac
97.	2012	J. Lochore	D. Lord
98.	2013	J. Strathern	D. Lord
99.	2014	J. King	D. Lord
100.	2015	J. C. Macaulay	D. Lord